The Forsaken Child

Benuel M. Fisher

THE FORSAKEN CHILD, by Benuel M. Fisher

ISBN 09766517-1-8 (pbk.)

Based on *Das verstossene Kind: Eine Geschichte für jung und alt, die vom Jahre 1862 in Russland anfängt; Es handelt sich um ein Kind, welches von allen verstossen und verachtet wurde*, by Wilhelm (Big Bill) J. Enns (Steinbach, Manitoba: Steinbach Post, 1944; reprint, Steinbach, Manitoba: Die Mennonitische Post, 2000); about Johann Peters, 1862 (or 1863?)–1946. The present work, *The Forsaken Child*, is presented with the knowledge and blessing of Harold A. Peters, a descendant of Johann Peters.

This book is a companion to one about another rejected child, *The Unwanted Son,* published by Benuel M. Fisher in 2003.

Book design by Garber Editing, 300 S. High St., Scottdale, PA 15683

Artwork on front and back covers suggested by the author

Paintings by Sylvia Fisher

Published by Benuel M. Fisher
722A Peters Road
New Holland, PA 17557

First printing 2005

Printed in the United States of America

Contents

Foreword by Peter J. Dyck v
Preface vii

1. Rescued from a Hog Pen 1
2. Aunt Sara as Wet Nurse 8
3. An Extra Village Meeting 15
4. His Name Is Johann 23
5. Baby Clothes Needed 29
6. "If I Ever Get Hold of That Child" 34
7. Trashed Again 42
8. "Does the Child Live?" 50
9. "Did They Find That Baby?" 53
10. With the Derksens 61
11. A Sad Death 64
12. The Second Wife 72
13. Pushed into the Creek 77
14. Hard School Days 82
15. The Teacher Punished 91
16. From Mother to Mother 95
17. Talking about America 100
18. Abandoned Again 106
19. Yet Another Mother 113
20. Off to Canada 121
21. The Girlfriend 133
22. Johann's Second Visit 140
23. Wedding Plans 147
24. Happily Married 154

cs ɛ

Foreword

This is an exciting and dramatic cliff-hanger. You start reading it and you can't stop. After a while you begin to wonder what horrible things could possibly happen to the poor little boy that haven't already happened.

I was ready to lay the book aside as fantasy, exaggeration, untrue. These are not the Mennonites in Russia that I know, that I am part of. In our community—Am Trakt, near the Volga River, where I was born and went to school until we emigrated to Canada when I was twelve years old—I never heard of anyone abandoning a child, just tossing it to the pigs. "Utterly impossible. This is not history; this is fiction," I thought.

But then I stopped to consider *when* all this is reported to have happened—in the early 1860s, not in the 1920s, when I went to school in Russia. I realized that I could be wrong. Instead of placing the events of the story in my time, I had to go back and place them into the time when our people in Russia were facing a problem similar to what they had faced in Prussia, which was part of the reason they migrated to Russia: *lack of land.*

Just as the Prussian government had forbidden our Mennonites to subdivide their land so that their sons could become farmers, so the Russian government also forbade the Mennonite immigrants to subdivide their land. Their farms in Russia generally had 176 acres. Mennonites usually had large families. In my family we were nine children, and in my wife's family were fourteen. If half of the children were boys, and their parents could not give them some of their land, what were they to do? The problem of the "landless" children was very real.

Take just one of the original four settlements in Russia as an example: Molotschna (the others were Chortitza, Am Trakt, and Alexandertal) in 1865 had 1,384 landed farmers and 2,356 landless workers. *The Mennonite Encyclopedia* says: "Only the landowners, comprising less than one-third of the population, had civic and economic rights; the other two-thirds had none."

Imagine a situation where your own grown-up children, not permitted to own land, live on the edge of the same village where their parents and relatives own land. They go to work for those landowners as common hired laborers, milking cows not theirs and cleaning rooms they do not own.

Before long the people realized that somehow they had to solve this ugly problem. Ministers and mayors put their heads together to find a solution. In 1863 they formed the Landlosen-Kommission (Landless Commission), which carefully studied the problem and proposed one solution: create a fund to buy land for their landless children.

They called these new areas "daughter settlements." The first was Bergthal, founded earlier, in 1836, with five villages. During the next 90 years, they established 48 daughter colonies with 287 villages. The new fund was a beautiful example of mutual aid. As they were able, the children who settled in the daughter colonies repaid the money the Kommission had loaned for their land. With this revolving fund, the Mennonites were able to continue purchasing more land.

When all this came to my mind and I put the picture of this forsaken child into the right perspective, I began to understand how all this could have happened in one of those early landless communities. Even so, it seems to me that in translating this true story the author no doubt shed some tears and likely found it hard to check some historical details, such as the government questioning the use of the Bible in schools. After 1917, during the 70 years of Communist rule, the Bible was removed from schools.

On the other hand, the frequent mention of prayer, the looking to God for help, and the intimate description of a loving and caring family are constantly refreshing and positive aspects of the otherwise horribly sad and shocking story.

—Peter J. Dyck
Longtime MCC worker and storyteller
Scottdale, Pennsylvania

☙ ❧

Preface

In February of 2004, a friend asked me to go along to a two-day auction in Kidron, Ohio. On a small table inside the building, I displayed copies of *The Unwanted Son*, which I published in 2003. It tells the story of a resident of Lancaster County, Pennsylvania, who experienced rejection and hardship in his childhood.

Hundreds of people walked by, and my sales were good. A gray-haired Mennonite lady stopped and told me, "I have that book in German."

This aroused my curiosity, and I replied, "I don't think so."

She said, "I'll bring it along tomorrow," and she did. But it was not a book I had published. Instead, the title was *Das verstossene Kind* (The Outcast Child), by Wilhelm (Big Bill) J. Enns.*

"May I read it?" I asked.

"Yes, but I want it back again," she answered.

Reading German was not new for me. That evening I began going through it. This book soon told me of another unwanted son, a sad story beginning in 1862 in Russia. Though some of the German words were strange to me, I had to go on reading the tale. I could not give up. "Surely this book cannot all be true," I thought.

On our homeward journey, a few friends suggested that I should translate this story into an English version. Somehow I had to locate the author for permission, but where would I find him? At last I discovered that he had passed away many years ago. But I received reports of this book still being printed for Mennonites in Mexico. Finally I talked with the printer by telephone. He said

---

* As identified on the copyright page, above.

that he did not know of any continuing copyright holder and encouraged me to proceed.

I spent many, many hours at my desk, searching through my German-English dictionary to grasp the meanings of words and sentences. It helped me present the proper meaning of the story, which I read two times before starting to write.

The Russian Mennonites would speak of a woman as "Frau Derksen," and call a man "Peters" or "Mayor Peters." To further identify the characters in the story, I have added some first names, such as for "Susanna Peters," to provide easier reading.

At times this task of translating and adapting the story was so complicated that I questioned why I ever attempted the task—something totally new for me. Was it another coincidence that through meeting this old lady, God reminded me to write another book?

Meanwhile, I have omitted a few matters of the original story that I thought sounded too harsh and rude. Instead, I have added background details and conversations to produce good moral reading of this true account, plus some extra comments or exhortations in distinctive type.

In February of 2005 while on a bus tour through parts of Mexico, I saw the homestead villages (*campos*) and also the lifestyles of these Mennonites, possibly some descendants of people you will read about in this book. I have changed a few names to discourage identification of certain characters in the story.

I also had the privilege of meeting the publisher of *Das verstossene Kind* and asked him, "Are all these happenings true?"

"Oh, yes, certainly," was his answer. "The child in this story was over eighty years old and still living when the account was first printed in 1944."

He explained: "Our ancestors are originally from the Anabaptist movement led by Menno Simons in the 1500s. Two hundred years later, many of them relocated to southern Russia. In the 1870s a migration of Mennonites moved from there to Canada, and in the 1920s thousands left for Mexico. Every movement was out of resistance to public school laws and the military draft."

This true story describes the early years of a child who at birth was cast out at the request of the birth mother. Nevertheless, the boy survived and had a hard, rude, and embarrassing early life.

The forsaken child joined a migration to southern Manitoba, Canada. He grew up and lived to be eighty-three. In his old age, many times he shuddered and tears rolled down his face as he told of his life. Other old men and women could also remember some of the sad happenings of his young life. They shared information to compile the original book *Das verstossene Kind.*

My reason for relating these incidents is not to disgrace or undermine the life of the Russian Mennonites. After all, some children experience rejection in various families and communities, as my first book showed for a setting in Lancaster County, Pennsylvania.

Instead, I intend this retold story to be good moral reading. It is an insistent warning to all teenagers to keep their lives pure and holy, and to parents and adults to love, accept, and treasure the children God gives us.

May I ask your forgiveness for any names, facts, or details that might be inaccurate, as shaped in translating and retelling this true story.

Give all honor to God.

—Benuel M. Fisher

Sylvia
05

❧ 1 ☙

Rescued from a Hog Pen

"Oh, my land!" exclaimed a young woman early one quiet morning. She was walking a back lane of Heuboden, a village in the Bergthal settlement of southern Russia.

"What do I hear?" The faint sound was that of a newborn creature. In a moment she focused her eyes toward the sound. Only a few yards away, in a sloppy manure yard, lay a little baby.

Immediately she climbed over the rough wooden rail fence. A big full-grown sow was also curious to know what was lying there. Her big snout was only a few inches away from the child, and she was ready to eat the little one.

Marie's heart was pounding with awful fear. She screamed and gave the huge four-legged beast a tremendous kick with her bare foot, right upon its nose. The woman's fear was so great that she did not feel the intense pain from her foot hitting the snout.

The hog screamed and watched with savage-looking eyes, ready to attack this intruder. In the wink of an eye, as the sow charged after her, the young childless woman grabbed the infant out of the filth and scrambled over the fence again.

Without thinking about the hog manure on the baby, she pressed the scantily clad infant against her bosom and cried in grief: "How did you get here, you poor creature? Surely no mother in this village would abandon her newborn baby in such a cruel way, by feeding it to the hogs!"

With these confused thoughts, she pulled her sweater over the baby to keep it warm and held it tightly against her bosom. In fear, she ran toward her home, hoping no one would see her.

She entered the house and laid what she thought must be the lowliest child on earth upon a bench beside the brick stove, where people placed things that needed heat or drying. So now this dirty-looking baby needed warmth. Marie did not know how long it had been lying in the hog yard that chilly morning in early April.

Quickly she brought a clean blanket. She knew the babe was still breathing, but perhaps it was too nearly frozen to utter any more sounds.

As she wrapped the soft blanket around the infant, she took it on her lap. And then amid the dried manure on the baby, she noticed a piece of narrow cloth tied tightly around its neck. Quickly she tore it off, and the infant exhaled a louder whimper and began breathing more normally.

Marie again laid the precious bundle on the wooden bench while she went to get a bit of milk. She poured the milk into a small pan and set it on the stove, to warm up.

She was so excited and distracted by care and fear for having someone's abandoned baby in her house. Marie prayed earnestly to God to calm her fears, asking what she should do first in this unusual situation. In no way was this woman or her husband prepared for this.

"O, Lord, please send John home before the dinner hour," she prayed as she started feeding the infant by dropping a teaspoonful of warm milk into its mouth. She cautiously dripped a few drops at a time on its tongue.

Soon the babe was moving its tongue, so Marie sensed that it was swallowing the milk. But she did not want to give it too much, fearing it might get sick. She wished she could nurse the baby.

Then she brought a warm, wet washcloth and cleaned the filth off the baby's face and partly bald head. She could hardly control her nerves, but she could feel the hand of God leading her. As she held the infant tightly upon her bosom, she cried a few tears of love as she looked into the sweet, innocent face.

"Less than ten minutes ago, I found this precious little darling," she said quietly as she placed a sweet kiss on his forehead.

"Oh my, am I doing the right thing, keeping this tiny infant in our house by myself?" She took the sleeping baby into the bedroom and placed it gently on her bed. "Suppose it would die. Others might accuse me of destroying the life of some mother's baby. Oh, how I wish John were at home!"

The warm infant began to move its little arms and cry

faintly. Soon it fell asleep. For quite a while, Marie stood beside the bed, looking at the foundling. All kinds of thoughts raced through her mind.

"After seven years of marriage, John and I so much wished for a child, and now here one is perhaps given to us through the hand of God," she mused. Tears rolled down her cheeks, dripping off her nose and onto the blanket in which the babe was wrapped. "We often prayed that if God would share only one child with us, we would be well satisfied, if that is God's will."

In her excitement she had not noticed whether the baby was a boy or a girl, but she knew it was alive. Her head swirled with questions as she quietly went back to the kitchen again, hoping somehow to relax her nerves.

Marie just could not imagine what horrible feelings a woman in her right mind could have that would lead her to desert her newborn infant. And then to tie a tight cloth around its neck and throw it into the hog pen—how awful! She shivered and cried and then thought, "Might some ungodly person have snatched this newborn from the mother? Either way, this is a terrible sin."

Her mind was churning: "God will not permit any such person to pass through the pearly gates into heaven if they destroy a sweet little angel in the first hours of his life.

"With all his power, King Herod tried to destroy the infant baby Jesus, but he did not find him. And so he ordered his soldiers to kill all the little children of Bethlehem less than two years of age. God had a reason to protect the baby Jesus from death the same as he had for me to rescue the foundling from the hog yard."

Many questions prodded Marie's confused mind: "Was this little child also born in a stable, as Jesus was? Where is its mother and father? Are they of the very poor folks living in our area? Did they think they could not afford to feed or clothe this child as it grows up? If the parents would ask God for advice and guidance, he would surely provide a way not foreseen to them."

"I cannot handle this situation any longer," she told herself. "I must go to the neighbor lady, but I do not trust leaving the child alone in this house."

Early that morning her twenty-nine-year-old husband, John, had gone to the neighboring village, looking for work to provide food for his wife and himself. They were of the Russian Mennonites who at that time lived mostly in poverty and wished for any kind of work. Jobs were hardly available anywhere. Many folks like John and Marie had only a small plot for a garden and owned only one cow.

In their young working years, they did not think of any luxury or extra money. When the summer growing season was bad, many families in the settlement's villages shared supplies with each other.

If John found work anywhere, he often did not return till evening, rather than walking quite a distance home for dinner. So Marie did not know when he would arrive. Just in case he came at noon, she decided to cook a few potatoes and prepare something. She nervously set the potatoes on the table.

"He must come," she insisted to herself as she went back into the bedroom to see if the child was still sleeping. For a long time she stood beside the bed, looking at this innocent sleeping child. Suddenly her whole body trembled as she heard a noise in the kitchen. Quickly she went to see what it might be.

There stood her husband. Right off, by looking at her disturbed face, he knew that something out of the ordinary had happened.

"Marie, is something wrong?" he asked. "Tell me quickly. What has happened to you?"

Marie could not talk. She was speechless and could not utter a sound. Suddenly she burst out crying, her nervous arms twitching.

As fear gripped his spirit, John hugged her. "Marie, tell me what is wrong. Are you sick?"

Finally she could relax herself enough to say, "No, no, dear John. I am not sick. But what has happened to me this morning, I will not be able to forget as long as I live on this earth. Come—I will show you." She took his hand and led him into the bedroom.

"Well, Marie, what is this?" asked John, bewildered, as he saw the infant lying in their bed. "Whose baby is it, and why are you so alarmed about it? Is it dead?"

"Oh my, John!" she exclaimed. "I have experienced something awful this morning. After you left the village, I suddenly decided to take a walk to Giesbrechts, taking the back lane. As I walked by the fourth barnyard, which is that dirty, sloppy hog pen, I heard a tiny whimper before the sun beamed its first rays.

"It was a sound that grabbed my attention. As I looked where the cry came from, I noticed this tiny form lying in the hog yard, right inside the old rail fence and only a few yards away. Immediately I scrambled over the fence into the slop as I saw an old sow coming toward it.

"As you know, pigs' habit is to have a dry place in their pen to lie down and sleep. They also have another corner where they drop their manure. Perhaps the huge sow did not notice the infant, but she noticed me. I gave her a tremendous kick on her nose, then quickly snatched the baby out of the manure.

"With the baby in my arms, I crawled back over the fence so quickly that I hardly remember how I did it. I feared that my bare feet would slip in the slop and I might drop the baby. It all happened so suddenly that I didn't think of asking for God's help until I was outside the pen again.

"Then I wrapped my sweater around the babe and ran toward home. The errand I had intended this morning turned out so opposite from what I had planned."

Marie showed her husband the cloth that had been tied around the baby's neck. She turned the infant on his back so John could see the little face. They both looked at the helpless child, speechless and in deep thought as they stood at the bedside for quite a while.

Finally John said, "But Marie, we are not able to care for this child. You cannot nurse it. It needs a mother's milk."

Marie unwrapped the blanket a trifle more, and John noticed the dry manure on the baby. "Don't you think you should wash it clean?" John asked.

The sloppy manure had oozed through the thin blue fabric around the tiny body.

"I thought about it," Marie admitted, "but I was too shook up that I could hardly do anything to help it except give it some cow's milk."

Marie took the tiny baby in her arms. She unwrapped the

blanket and laid it upon the warm bench by the stove while John heated a small basin of water. She bathed it gently and exclaimed, "It's a little boy!"

They both shed tears of joy but could not relax. "O God," Marie cried, "if this is your will, we will be so happy to keep this precious soul."

After she finished cleaning every bit of scum from even the tiny little toes, she wrapped the infant in another soft, clean blanket and placed a soothing kiss on each cheek.

With bleeding hearts, both John and Marie were so confused as to what all this meant. Gently Marie carried the tiny bundle back to the bedroom. They both knelt beside the bed while John prayed earnestly to God to give them wisdom so they would know how to cope with this matter. John thought of the wisdom God had given to King Solomon on a decision about two babies.

As they rose to their feet again, Marie laid the baby on the bed and said, "I need to prepare dinner for us. It's beyond our noon mealtime."

John stayed at the bedside, looking and in deep thought about how the baby Jesus was the promised child for many years. But to whom was this child promised? He had no answer.

Marie called, "Dinner is ready, John. We need to eat before we decide anything more about this situation. Depending on how things turn out today yet, we might not be home this evening."

Again, they bowed their heads in prayer as they sat at the table, bewildered. As they ate dinner, they spoke few words.

After dinner Marie gently sat on a chair beside the warm stove, with the sleeping infant cuddled against her bosom. John stood at her shoulder.

"Oh, John," cried Marie, with warm tears rolling down her face, "I just can't understand who would throw her little baby to the hogs. If I would not have taken it away from the big sow, she would surely have eaten it."

"Marie," said John, "you are a God-sent angel. God needed you to destroy and defeat the plans of this ungodly mother. We don't know who she is, but God does. I think it is best that we never find out. In this way, we will not know who to blame and can feel more comfortable raising this child.

"Look at it this way. God possibly knew the boy would have a sad life as a child. Do you believe it is God's plan that innocent children must suffer? All children need the love of a mother to help make them able to be servants of God someday.

"Let us pray for the mother who committed this awful sin, that she might repent someday. As long as she does not repent, she will carry this terrible guilt as long as she lives.

"I doubt that she will live many years because this guilty feeling will ruin her health. If she is unhealthy for a number of years, she will struggle many days and nights with evil thoughts. No doubt with tears from not being forgiven, she will confess on her deathbed to someone.

"So Marie, give yourself up to be a maidservant, as Mary did to be the mother of Jesus."

"Yes, I want to be his mother," consented Marie. "But how shall we feed him?"

Then the infant moved his tiny arms. Soon he began whimpering and crying much louder than before. Marie trembled and felt so helpless because she could not nurse the little darling.

His crying aroused John from his distant thoughts. "I'm going to the village mayor for advice," he said. "I will ask him if he knows of anyone who is missing a baby. Surely if some child is lost, the whole village will know about it by now."

John grabbed his felt cap and left the house.

ଓ 2 ଷ

Aunt Sara as Wet Nurse

Soon after John left the house, he remembered Marie's aunt, on the third street. "Isaac Harders have a newborn baby only a few weeks old," he thought. "Her true love will not let this foundling go hungry. I know she will come and nurse the baby for us."

Marie stayed sitting by the stove as the baby began to cry again. She sensed that he was hungry. "Oh, how I wish I could satisfy your hunger. I love you so dearly." She held him tightly, fearing that he might be taken away from her.

"Please, God, let me keep this precious darling," she prayed softly as she got up to carry him around, hoping to quiet him.

She heard a knock on the door and expected John to be back. Instead, it was Aunt Sara Harder.

"Hello, Marie. Now what is this that your husband told me about? Is it true?"

"Yes," Marie replied as she opened her arms and showed the little baby to her dear friend. Now again, she cried and cried in front of her well-loved aunt.

"As your husband was on his way to the village mayor, he stopped by, asking me to come over as soon as possible to help you with a little child. He didn't take much time explaining the situation, but I gathered that it is something that I should check out. As soon as our little Jacob fell asleep, I promptly walked over. Whose child have you found?"

Marie briefly told Sara about her experience. "It was early this morning when I found him. I only gave him a bit of cow's milk by dropping it into his mouth. I think he is hungry. Would you nurse him, please?"

"Oh, sure," agreed Sara. "Let me have the little fellow." She had no problem in getting the hungry darling to nurse. In a few moments the neglected baby began moving his tiny arms and feet while swallowing the warm milk.

"He seems to be a strong baby. How long do you think he was lying out in the cold slop?" asked Sara.

"I have no idea," answered Marie as she told Sara all the details of rescuing the infant and tried to explain her terrible inward feelings. "How would you feel, Aunt Sara? I am just so glad you are here to comfort me. My nerves are throbbing in my whole body. Your sweet presence helps me to relax."

"Yes, I know this is a very unusual happening," Sara consoled her. "But submit yourself to what God has planned for you and where he will lead you. We must all be willing to help others, no matter what lies before us.

"I definitely believe God led you through the back lane this morning to save this little child. You are not at fault. You did not try to destroy his life. You saved his life, and therefore you might be able to raise him as your own child. I doubt that anyone will object to you and John keeping this sweet infant. I know you love him already as if he were your own."

"Yes, I do," agreed Marie. "But why could not someone else have found him, someone able to nurse him? Right now Bessie, our cow, does not give much milk. We can hardly afford to buy any. You know that milk is very scarce in our village because the herder does not do a good job with the cows in the far-off fields. They hardly find any grass yet. It's too cold."

"Marie, Marie, don't let your thoughts trouble you so badly," said Sara as the little darling was snoozing softly upon his nurse's breast. "If the mayor calls a meeting about this incident, I'll tell my husband to say that we will care for this baby. Our Jacob is only ten days older, and I will also nurse your baby for you."

Marie felt comforted as she took the little one into her open arms. She kept gazing upon the sweet face. Finally the two walked into the small bedroom that was unprepared for this infant. She gently laid him on their double bed.

As both women sat in the kitchen, Marie asked, "Sara, what would you do in my position?"

"Please, Marie, don't worry about it," urged Sara. "Trust that God wanted you folks to have this child. Surely you and John have often prayed that God would bless you with children. Now, if the good Lord in heaven saw—and I'm sure he did—this tiny newborn baby being thrown to the hogs, I honestly think he planned that someone would find it and care for it. You are a lifesaving woman. Please accept this gift without fear.

"Well, I have been here much longer than I had planned. I must go and see if little Jacob is still sleeping.

"Do you remember the little baby Moses we read about in the Bible? Pharaoh's daughter found him floating in a basket, and she asked a Hebrew mother to care for him. I will do the same for you and nurse your baby."

Marie willingly trusted God to provide a way for her. She watched from the window as Sara walked down the village street. "A blessed woman," she mused to herself.

A while later John came back, and as soon as he entered the kitchen, he said, "The mayor has planned a meeting at his house this evening at eight o'clock, to find out whose child it is, or if anyone has any clues. The news is spreading through the village like a forest fire. People are confused and alarmed that anybody in this village would be so cruel and evil. We will see what the people decide."

All kinds of ideas were running through Marie's mind, and she could not relax. John decided to stay in the house with her the rest of the afternoon, helping with her housework.

It was a long day for the couple, and the clock seemed to stand still. Finally evening came, and their cow was not in the village yet. As they waited, leaning against the barnyard gate, they looked out to see if the village herdsman was coming with the cows.

In the Russian settlements in the nineteenth century, it was a custom to have a herdsman or shepherd taking all the cattle owned by poor villagers, caring for them during the day, and trying to find some grass for them in nearby areas. In dry seasons he needed to walk the herd quite a distance for grazing. From the time they were calves, these cows were used to this routine of walking with their herder.

Mark, the herder, was not very dependable. While going through the village with the cattle, he gossiped with everybody he met. Thus, the cows often came in late and still had to be milked. After the long, cold winter, there was hardly any feed in the village. The people depended mostly on the hillside grazing.

For the most part, these poor folks had their small house and barn built together, sometimes under the same roof. A narrow fenced-in barnyard was between the barn and the street. As the herder came down the street, every cow knew where her gate was and turned in to be milked.

Some of these villagers had a few hogs, which they always kept in the barnyard at the rear. This way the hog manure did not create a bad odor for folks walking along the street.

A dozen or so hens were fenced in a small yard, to provide eggs for a few families. The hens also ate grass and leftover garden vegetables if any were available. They laid eggs only during the spring and summer months. In the cold, dreary winter months, they had only enough energy to stay alive.

These poor peasants ate and saved what they had. There simply were no luxuries, and choice foods were unknown. They depended on God rather than on management and money. Even so, they were satisfied with what they had and enjoyed fellowship together, sharing their extras.

John stood impatiently by the barnyard fence, waiting for his cow. He had much on his mind as the evening wore on. "Enough of this foolish herdsman," he told Marie. "I'm going to see what's keeping him." He started up the gravel and dirt street, then called back, "If Mrs. Harder comes before I get back, I'll milk Bessie. You go and take care of the baby. It's getting dark."

Marie was still very tense, watching her husband march up the street. She went into the kitchen. Soon Sara Harder came by, and Marie handed her the crying child.

"Oh, you little sweetie! Are you hungry again?" Sara said as she took him in her arms. She sat down to nurse him, asking, "Where is John going? As I came down the side street, I saw him running. He jumped over the gate at the end of the street. Did something happen again?"

"Well, he is quite upset about old Mark bringing the cattle in so late," Marie reported. "You know the meeting tonight starts at eight. He's afraid many of the folks will be late.

"On Monday Mark experienced some unusual situation. He always thinks he must tell everyone along the street as he brings the village cattle home. He's such a gossiper, you know."

"Yes," said Sara, "last evening when my husband met him at the farm gate, Mark was saying how a two-year-old bull got mad and tried to buck him down. Mark knew he had no way to defend himself other than to use his long hickory staff.

"He claims he gave the bull three mighty hard whops over his head as the bull charged him the second time. The angry beast fell to the ground and stayed flat for two hours. Who knows what to believe of the old herdsman if no one else saw it? Some say half of his stories aren't true."

"Yeah, so what?" protested Marie. "His job is to bring the cattle to the village on time, instead of fussing and gossiping with everyone he meets. That's why he's always late."

"Well, I think they will also discuss that at the meeting tonight," said Sara. "If he will not promise to do his job right, the village will hire another herder."

Marie changed the subject. "I don't like to leave the infant in the house alone. I'd feel responsible for him if anything should happen. John is not used to milking Bessie. She is used to soft woman's hands. For some reason, she kicks when John milks her."

Finally, the slender spotted cow strode into the barnyard, and John sat on the three-legged wooden milk stool to milk her. The old cow with her pointed horns turned her head to see who was squeezing out her milk. The rough, chapped hands annoyed her.

The bottom of the tin bucket was barely covered with milk when she bawled loudly, lifted her left foot, and struck her opponent a hard blow in the chest. That sent him flying backward off the stool. The battered milk bucket went flying, and the white liquid spritzed over John's face and gray shirt.

Marie could not keep from laughing as she approached the scene at that very moment. "O, Bessie! You're quite a character. What ails you? John won't hurt you."

Quickly she grabbed the bucket and sat down to milk her. Bessie stood there, content, as Marie's soft, gentle hands touched her teats. This irked John as he watched with angry eyes while cleaning the sticky milk from his face and beard with his hankie.

"Pfui, ugh, yuck! You stinker! No way will I milk you again

till you are dry after this lactation," he growled as he left the stall. He had had enough troubles today without this ignorant cow.

The sun had long been down. It was dark, and these folks carried no lantern in the barn.

As soon as Marie was finished milking, she entered the house. Sara Harder was ready to leave, saying, "I just got done feeding your sweet infant. He burped nicely, and I laid him down now. He's breathing softly, and I sense that you have a healthy infant in your house. Give him a warm bath yet tonight.

"Well, I must get home to remind my husband that he shall voice his opinion quite strongly at the meeting that we will help to care for this castaway baby. I have enough milk for him and our little Jacob, I'm sure."

As John walked into the dimly lighted kitchen, Marie said, "John, it's past seven thirty. I think you'd better hurry. Next you'll be late. Depending on how many curious folks gather this evening, you might not be able to get inside, and no one will realize that you know all about this."

"Now relax, Marie. Didn't we decide to let the good Lord on high handle this situation? I'm hungry, but I'll eat when I get back. Anyhow, I'm too emotional to keep anything down now."

Uncle Isaac Harder soon met John in the street, and together they headed for the mayor's house, where the villagers held all their meetings. They walked partway in silence and deep thoughts.

Then John said, "I wonder if many of the village folks heard about this little baby Marie found this morning. I sure hope we will not have any disputes about this child. I have had a hard day, with all kinds of worries. Suppose someone else says, 'It's our child'? I am all nervous and weary. I really wish we'd know whose child it is, and that they'd say we may keep it as our own."

Suddenly he remembered how only ten minutes ago he had told Marie to rely on God and pray while the meeting was in session. "Trust God," he had reminded her.

"Now look here," Isaac said. "My wife told me that when the question 'Who will care for this baby?' comes up, I shall say that we will. I intend to show the crowd tonight that I will take all the responsibility upon myself. If no one claims it or has no way of identifying it, that settles the matter right off."

As the two approached Mayor Peters' drive, they saw a big crowd of solemn people outside, rather quiet, talking in hushed voices. Some had no idea what this extra meeting on a Wednesday evening was about, after their regular monthly meeting only two days earlier, on Monday evening. They expected that this must be a difficult case, needing immediate discussion.

☙ 3 ❧

An Extra Village Meeting

After the folks had all assembled inside and were seated, the mayor sat at the table and turned up the wick of the kerosene lamp. In that time oil lamps were the brightest lights known. Often folks turned them down to save oil. In a dim house, people did not see shadows. The villagers hardly knew of reading by lamplight.

The big mantel clock chimed eight times. "Friends and neighbors," said Mayor Peters, "I know this is a surprise that I called a meeting again tonight. We just had our monthly meeting on Monday evening.

"But we have a case tonight that has never happened before in this village. It is quite sad and heartrending to speak of a newborn baby that was found in Reimers' hog pen this morning, a little after daybreak.

"Possibly many of you know of it already, but maybe some don't. Mrs. John Derksen heard its faint cry as she walked the back lane, taking a shortcut to the Giesbrechts."

Whispered voices were heard through the crowd. "What! John Derksen found a baby?"

"No, not John. His wife, Marie Derksen, found it and took it to her home," reported the mayor.

"We are gathered tonight to hear if anyone in this village knows whose child it might be. Does anyone have any clues as to who might have delivered it and helped the mother, or who and where the mother might be?"

"Is John's wife here?" asked Mayor Peters as he arose from his chair, rather nervous.

"No, but John is sitting over here," said Isaac Harder, pointing to John.

Mayor Peters searched the crowd in the dimly lighted room, with low ceilings and only two windows. The air was stuffy from the room being packed full of curious people.

"Now, John Derksen," urged the mayor. "I ask you to stand up and tell us about this complicated event. Then we will decide how to proceed further."

John slowly got to his feet, sensing all eyes focused on him. He felt weak, his heart was thumping with excitement, and his head hung low.

He shivered with horrible thoughts: "Just suppose someone blames me for kidnapping this infant and only making a story out of how Marie found it." He felt quite secure that all the people in this peaceful village of two hundred were Christians, but then, "Why would anyone abuse a newborn baby, planning to have it digested in the stomach of a big sow? Surely this was all planned, but who and where is the culprit?"

Before he spoke in the meeting, he sent up a quiet prayer: "Oh, please, Lord, help me in this awful moment. You know what the very truth is. Can I rely on you?"

The entire room was hushed and quiet. No feet shuffled. The audience waited motionless as John wiped tears from his cheeks. Many women wept tears of sadness.

Finally John's speech came forth: "Yes, it is true, what Mayor Peters said, that my wife found this baby boy in the sloppy hog pen, with a cloth tied tightly around its neck, likely to keep it from crying or else to choke it.

"Apparently every family in this village has children except for Marie and me. Hardly any of you know the heartaches Marie has had, wishing to have a child. You did not hear us complain. So I assume that you did not realize how it hurt her to see mothers with another newborn baby among her good friends of this village, while she stood by with empty arms, her heart crying, and yet a smile upon her face.

"We would be so happy to keep the foundling. We prefer to think that this was God's plan, that we might have one child, but Marie is not able to nurse him. So what shall we do?" With these words, John sank to his seat.

Deep sorrow filled the room. For a time no one spoke. Then Mayor Peters, with deeply wrinkled eyebrows, arose from his chair. His eyes focused straight forward.

"Well, folks, I assume that most of you heard what John

said. My first question is this: Does anyone in this room know more about this infant child? Speak up! We need to decide now who will take this child and care for him as an adopted son and raise him to manhood."

Men and women began whispering to one another:

"I don't feel that we want this baby if it was meant to be murdered."

"We have enough children of our own to feed."

"Someday he might be a very disobedient boy."

"Now, who of you will take this child," asked Mayor Peters quite firmly. "This is why you were called together tonight."

From the far end of the room, a voice was heard. "If Marie Derksen found it in the first place, why should not Johns be entitled to keep the child? It belongs to them."

Everyone watched for the mayor's response, with all eyes straight forward. He stretched his hand nervously and pushed the oil lamp a bit. Apparently he did not favor this suggestion. Then he spoke outright, his cheeks twitching in the dim room.

"Now, Kerle, we all know that Marie cannot nurse the baby, and the young infant is not able to eat rye and barley bread. Even a blind man can know that. If we do not care for the baby, our village will have a bad reputation of not treating infants properly."

In this village, folks knew little of bottle-feeding since milk from cows was scarce. Everyone was in deep thought. No feet shuffled. The room was dead still.

Isaac Harder was rubbing his big brawny hands, thinking deeply on this situation. Praying silently for wisdom, he rose to his feet and spoke:

"The way it appears, no one is willing to take any responsibility in supporting John and Marie to feed the infant. So we will take him for now. Our little Jacob is only ten days old. My wife has agreed to nurse both infants the same as any woman would with twins. When the child can eat bread, John and Marie will take him back.

"We accept this responsibility. On my way home, I will stop at John's house and tell my wife to take the child along home.

"We can't reject this little infant like a dog. He has a living soul, the same as any other child. The baby is totally innocent. If we leave him to die, we are doing the same as his real mother is possibly doing. Does anyone think well of such cruelty?" Isaac's voice became louder and louder as he spoke.

Finally the mayor was satisfied. "Yes, Mr. Harder, I think what you are saying is the very truth. I will not dispute your loving concern for this forsaken child. I think we all agree that you and Johns shall take the responsibility to care for the foundling. And the final decision is that John and Marie may keep him and raise him to manhood. Thank you, and God bless your home," added the mayor as he took his seat.

Now a question came forth: "What if the child's real mother hears of this adoption and tries to claim the child again?"

Isaac Harder stood up. "Beloved brothers and sisters of faith, let us all pray that God will not allow anything like that to happen. We need to concentrate on good thoughts and not evil ones. Please, let none of us as Christians say such a thing to John and Marie. They have enough stress to adjust to this mystery. Speak kind words of encouragement.

"Do unto them as you would have them do unto you. Isn't that the Golden Rule and also Jesus' Sermon on the Mount in Matthew, chapters 5 to 7?

"It is getting late, and my wife and Marie are alone in the house with the two babies. Please, folks, use common sense and not gossip about it wherever you go." This seemed to settle the matter.

Suddenly the herdsman stood up and started to talk at length about his adventure with the mad bull.

One of the men cut him off, saying, "Yeah, another thing we need to discuss is about Mark, our herder. Doesn't it matter that he comes so late with the cattle? Sometimes it is way late, beyond dark till he comes to our end of the village. It's very disgusting."

"Did something peculiar take place again today, or what do you have in mind?" asked the mayor.

"Here at your end of the village, the cattle come in on time. But by the time he has told all his funny stories to everyone he meets, it is way late at our end," said Isaac Harder.

"This is true," said Mayor Peters. "He has much to relate about his day's work. Who knows if it's all true, since he is by himself all day." The mayor turned to look at the herdsman.

"Now, Mark, you know what the folks expect of you. This evening you stood here talking for quite a while. Talking that much is not your job. Do your work promptly, and everyone will be satisfied. Otherwise, you'll lose your job."

"I'm very sorry," Mark apologized. "I promise to do a better job."

"Now, I think we have discussed everything this evening. Mr. Harder, you shall take the young infant along to your home and care for it," said the mayor. "And so the meeting is dismissed."

Quite often after the meetings, the village friends would visit, and laughter would explode among them. But this meeting was solemn, and folks were serious in their thoughts. There was not much commotion as they walked quietly down the streets in the cool night.

John Derksen and Isaac Harder walked swiftly together, yet at one point they paused to look at the many stars in the far-off sky. They thought of God and his great love. Surely their heavenly Father had planned the outcome of this meeting. John was so glad for Isaac's support and also that no one at the meeting had any dispute about the foundling.

Marie and Sara were sitting in the small kitchen, pondering and praying that God would rule the hearts of everyone present at the village meeting that night. The clock struck ten chimes. Usually they would be sound asleep by this time, but tonight sleep did not grip them.

The wooden door opened with a slight creak, and John and Isaac walked in. "You two still awake?" chided Ike. "Well, here is the good news.

"Marie, you are allowed to keep the baby. No complaints except that Mayor Peters agreed that if Sara and I have the infant in our house for now, Sara will nurse the baby till he is able to eat bread. Then you folks may keep him as your own child. You are responsible to feed and raise him. I'm sure you are willing to do everything that is a mother's duty."

Both babies were snuggled in the women's laps. Sara said, "It looks as though the two babies are much the same size, although our Jacob is ten days older. They're almost twins."

"You're right," said Uncle Isaac as he reached out his right hand. "Here, let me hold Jacob in my one hand and John's baby in my left hand. See if I can feel any difference in weight. . . . Nope, I think they must be the same."

Isaac took his cane and asked Marie for a basket to lay her infant in. He tied the basket to the end of the cane. "Bring me a half bucket of water," he requested, "and we will see which baby weighs the most. I know you have no scales since only a few of the more prosperous people in our village can afford any."

He grasped the cane at its center. "Now lay the baby in the basket, and I'll hook the bucket of water on the other end. See if they balance equally. If it does not balance level, John, pour a few more cups of water in the bucket. Okay, now it's perfectly level. Do you see?"

"Now take baby Jacob out and put the other baby in the basket. Let's see if it still balances."

It did not balance. The bucket was too heavy. John took the cup and began dipping out water, three cups full till the cane was level again. "That means a difference of one and a half pounds," declared Isaac.

You can see," said Isaac with a laugh, "the foundling is three cups lighter. So we can see which baby has the best mother! But if he gets good loving care and stays healthy, he will gain weight.

Now again, Marie began to lament about why she had to be the woman to find this baby early that morning and go through all this stress.

"Listen to me, Marie," Uncle Isaac answered seriously. "We don't understand nearly all the things in our life. God plans many hardships for us, and if we willingly accept them, afterward we will find a blessing. This will brighten our days again, and we may feel needed to do more for the unfortunate ones. We will never become poor by helping the despised folks.

"You and John are Christian folks, and I trust that you pray to the Lord every day to lead you. God rules your thoughts, giving you peace in your minds. Thus, we think God told you to go along the back lane this morning. Do you believe this?"

"Yes," answered Marie kindly.

"No one saw this baby lying in the hog yard except you," said Isaac. "We are only going by what you say. We know that you are not making up a story. If we trust you, then you also must trust God.

"Do you wish you would have let him lie there, that you would have just ignored this angel from heaven? The big sow surely would have torn it to pieces and eaten it, or else it would have frozen to death."

With these words of exhortation, Marie burst out sobbing, and the tears ran freely down her quivering cheeks. "No, no," she cried. "I'm glad I found it, but no one understands my grief. I want to be God's servant. Tell everyone to pray for us. God's will be done on earth as it is in heaven."

"Remember what I told you after dinner?" Sara asked. "I will care for your infant the same as I do for little Jacob. When he is able to eat bread and will not need to be breast-fed, you folks may have him in your home from then on.

"Be glad and content. Perhaps at this hour the mother who gave him birth might find out that her baby is still alive and will thank you for rescuing him from death. The mother could be a total stranger or an unmarried daughter who was burdened with a sin for which she felt there is no forgiveness."

If Marie had known who and where the real mother was, she would have had much more fear of accepting the foundling. Actually, the birth mother thought the infant was dead and was just then hearing that someone had found it. Her evil scheme did not work as she had planned. God had other plans.

"Yes, but we are so poor," Marie answered with concern. "We have barely enough to eat as it is. What will the people say if we have taken a little baby out of someone's hog pen?"

"Oh, Marie," pleaded Aunt Sara, "please don't think all the bad things. Surely the village folks would not accuse you for showing such kindness." Yet she knew a few people had already made such remarks about John and Marie.

John walked toward the stove and put more dried manure on the fire, to heat the room. They could not afford any coal or wood. As Marie saw John at the stove, she remembered that they had not eaten supper before going to the meeting.

"Pardon me, John. I was so distracted tonight. I simply forgot about supper. I'll prepare the table, and we'll eat before Uncle Isaac and Aunt Sara leave."

"No, no," said Sara, "it's too late for you to make supper for us. After such a stressful day as both of you have endured, you are ready for bed. I am also so tired from all these difficult decisions we've had to make that I don't feel hungry at all. How about you, Isaac?"

"I agree," remarked Isaac. "Marie looks so awfully tired and weary. I'd rather do without supper. I'm sure this was the hardest day in your young life, but remember that you are bound to have some more hard days. The only way through is to totally rely on the hand of God."

"Aunt Sara, you have been such a great help to me many times since my mother passed away three years ago," said Marie. "Thank you for being such an understanding person. Is this how God answered my prayers at mother's death? Mother would be glad to see that we may have a child to claim as our own."

She went to the cellar to fetch a jar of canned peas. "I will soon make toasted bread and pea soup, and you two will stay and eat with us," pleaded Marie.

"Okay, Marie, we'll accept your kindness," Isaac said.

After a scanty and late supper, Sara said, "We must get home to our children. They'll be alarmed and wondering why the meeting adjourned so late. Here, Ike, you take little Jacob, and I'll carry John and Marie's baby. Good night. We'll see each other tomorrow sometime."

They each wrapped their infant in a blanket and walked toward home in the cold breeze of the dark night.

☙ 4 ❧

His Name Is Johann

The moment the Harders stepped out of the house into the starlit night, they saw the figure of a young woman dodge away from the side window. She ran along the weathered picket fence toward the garden gate and was immediately lost in the darkness.

This scene caused their blood to freeze. Their thoughts turned to fear as they wondered if someone had been watching them from outside the window. Silently they trembled as both clutched the babies to their bosoms.

They did not want to turn back to tell John and Marie about the sighting, fearing that would only create more misery for them. The Harders exchanged a few words and kept praying that this sly woman would not disturb John's home during the night.

"Could that possibly be the mother of this baby you are carrying?" asked Isaac. "This is quite a mystery. I rather dread this situation. I feel so tired and weary from this long day. It's nearly midnight. I have a strong feeling that the birth mother is still trying to destroy her newborn son. I wonder if she was at the meeting this evening."

"No, Isaac, I doubt very much that she would be able to run around like that if she gave birth to the baby only last night," said Sara. "She would need to rest. Perhaps another woman or her mother might be involved. But I definitely feel that no grandmother could bear to have her sweet little grandchild harmed in any way. She just couldn't. Such women are servants of the devil.

"Remember how we both reminded John and Marie to pray and trust in the Lord? Now *we* are failing to trust."

They both felt quite relieved to reach their door and enter their dark house.

"This incident reminds me of how Mary and Joseph carried the baby Jesus to Egypt in the dark night, when King Herod was looking for a chance to destroy the Holy Child," said Isaac. "Many innocent babies under the age of two were pulled out of crying mothers' arms to be slaughtered and murdered because Jesus was born a king. Years later he suffered and died for our sins, but not for the innocent little children. They had no sins."

A sign of relief escaped from Sara as she unfolded the blanket from the still nameless infant. It was past midnight, and she thought the children were all asleep. Soon the new baby cried loudly. Their oldest daughter, Katharina, awoke and heard the cry of an infant she knew was not her little brother.

At this late hour, Isaac and Sara had moved quietly so as not to arouse any of the children and have to face difficult questions. They were ready for rest.

Katharina emerged from the room where the six children slept. This house also was small, with no upstairs rooms. She gazed with wide-open eyes to see mother and father both holding a baby.

"See here, you have another little brother," Sara told her as she handed the foundling to her.

"Mother, where did you get it? Surely it's not yours!" exclaimed Katharina as she caressed the tiny infant in her skinny arms.

Again the hungry infant cried. "O baby dear, don't make such an ugly face. I love you. Mother, whose baby is it? Tell me quickly." She had more questions than her mother could answer.

Their conversation woke her nine-year-old sister, Lenchen. Wearing her ragged and faded nightgown, she rubbed her sleepy eyes as she walked to her mother and complained, "Why are you so loud? I can't sleep." Suddenly she spied the two babies and heard them whimpering, and her brown eyes beamed back and forth in each direction.

"Mother, whose tiny baby does Katharina have?" she asked as she stuck her curious nose right down to the baby's sweet face.

She wanted to hold the newborn, but Katharina suggested, "No, Lenchen, please don't disturb it, so it won't cry again. Mother is very tired. Tomorrow we can hold both this one and little Jacob."

Not satisfied, Lenchen asked, "Mom, where did you get

another little baby? Do we have twins? Oh, how great!" She looked again at her little brother Jacob. "They look so cute, both the same size."

"No, Lenchen," said Isaac. "Our little Jacob is three cups heavier. We checked it out over at John and Marie's house this evening."

Both girls laughed sweetly as their straggly pigtails hung loosely down their backs, each delighted to be holding a baby.

"If we love and care for both of them alike, I think they will soon be the same weight and size," their mother assured them.

"Is this our baby? May we keep it?" asked Lenchen as she hugged and kissed the newborn.

"Now, girls, it's time you go back to bed. You may hold him tomorrow morning again."

The nine- and twelve-year-old girls hopped into their bed beside their three-year-old sister. They could not sleep right away but kept whispering big dreams about their future days.

Sara nursed both babies again, the new baby first, and then she barely had enough to satisfy her own. She now fully realized the great responsibility she had. While nursing, she prayed, asking God to support her with strength and also that she might be able to sleep till morning.

Before she dozed off to sleep beside her relaxed husband, Sara again thought of the baby's birth mother. Although they had earlier offered their daily evening prayer with the two girls, she still prayed to a merciful God, that he would forgive and lead this childless mother's thoughts unto repentance.

Tears of deep sorrow squeezed from Sara's closed eyes as the clock struck one in the hushed kitchen. Isaac had locked the front and the back doors. Finally the long day ended, and the house was dark.

Early the next morning, the two girls were awake again before daybreak. Remembering the event of the last night, they hustled to get dressed and aroused the other children out of their straw-tick beds.

Since they were already scrambling to get dressed, Mother did not need to call anyone. Seeing the sisters' excitement, the little boys knew something was astir. There were no light switches or flashlights, only one faint coal-oil lamp for the entire family.

As the two girls hurriedly slipped their unbuttoned dresses over their heads, the boys also entered the cold kitchen, half dressed, with pants partly unbuttoned. From the noisy commotion, the new baby soon began screaming, wakening the still-sleepy parents.

In the dimly lighted room, they could not see which was the new baby. Only by his crying could they know it was not baby Jacob.

"Why are you up so early?" protested the mother. "We hoped that we could sleep longer after getting to bed so late."

"Whose baby is here?" asked four-year-old Peter.

"Well, Peter, come and see. You have another baby brother," said Sara as she took the newborn from the tiny straw-tick bed where the two babies slept alongside the parents' bed.

Sara showed Peter the supposedly day-old infant. She did not know exactly when he was born, only that Marie had found him yesterday. The adults sensed that, by all appearances, the baby had been born only the night before Marie found him.

"Oh, Mama," chattered Peter, smiling, "what's his name?" It is a question little children usually first think to ask.

"Well, we didn't decide yet. We'll discuss that at the breakfast table."

Peter stroked the soft rosy cheeks as he stared, wide-eyed.

Sara stayed in the bedroom, nursing the new infant. She had decided always to feed him first, to make sure he got enough, and thus eliminating any unforeseen problems or questions about favoritism for her own baby.

Again, her thoughts went to his mother: "Is she suffering from not nursing her baby? Did she possibly die from childbirth at a very young age, and then her own mother felt that she would not be able to care for it? Where is the father of this child?"

Immediately she caught control of her brooding thoughts, which threatened to drag her down. She closed her eyes and focused in her mind a picture of a young mother lying awake all night, crying and praying to Jesus, confessing that she was sorry for abandoning her sweet infant in the hog pen. While Katharina was helping the other children get dressed, she told her oldest brother to fetch wood to start a fire before a late breakfast.

An hour after daybreak, Isaac brought the milk in, and soon the family was seated at the breakfast table, all except the mother. She was trying to satisfy her own hungry Jacob. Little Peter ran into the bedroom again. He was so excited about these two babies that he could hardly eat. Peter insisted on getting a better look at his new brother, now by the sunlight beaming through the east window.

As Sara had finished nursing both hungry babies, she finally sat at the table with the rest of her family. Already she was tired and yet happy with all the excitement of the cheery-eyed children. Sara knew she must eat a big breakfast to gain enough energy to provide for her volunteered task of nursing two babies.

Fried cornmeal mush, three eggs to divide with the family of eight at the table, plus bread and warm milk and hot tea—this provided a good healthy breakfast most every morning. Dinner and supper consisted of garden vegetables and small portions of meat, which flavored the hot soup of watered milk. Rather often milk was scarce, and the family wished for more.

"Now, children, how do you wish to name the little one?" asked Sara.

"Frank, Frank," yelled Peter.

Katharina looked at him. "No, that's an old name. Herman would suit lots better for him." She poured a cup of steaming tea.

"No, no, children, none of those names belong in the Harder family," observed Sara. "I think we should call him Johann [John]."

"Yes, Johann shall be his name," declared their father as he reached for a piece of barley bread. "Mother, why don't we have something special yet this morning in celebration for baby Johann?"

"Sure," said Sara. "You may each have one piece of barley bread and one of rye bread."

As they finished eating, the family bowed their heads low, saying grace, their daily routine at the end of every meal.

"Now, children," said Isaac, "we want to tell you who this little baby belongs to."

These six children, aged two to twelve, could not all grasp

the horrifying details. Their curious eyes focused straight at their father as tiny tears rolled over their cheeks. As he finished, their fearful hearts turned to joy at having a new brother.

Nevertheless, when their mother explained her love for John and Marie, that they might have the baby when he is able to eat bread, the children did not dispute a single word about the matter.

She explained how Marie's heart was touched when she found this little baby in a hog pen, with a sow about to destroy him. Sara also reminded them of a Bible story, how Pharaoh's daughter's heart was changed when she found the little baby Moses in the bulrushes. Likewise, Pharaoh had wanted to destroy Moses.

"Accepting but then countering an intended evil act will bring an abundance of joy to your heart," their father said. "This is only through God's love. So we will love Johann and give him a home while he is with us."

After the table was cleared, dishes washed, and all their chores finished, the four oldest children begged to go along the back lane to see where the baby was found. The hog pen looked like a horrifying place for a baby. They couldn't bear to look at that dirty place for long. Twelve-year-old Katharina grasped more of these details than the rest, and her young mind was stunned.

ঙ 5 ঌ

Baby Clothes Needed

While Isaac Harder walked through the village to the mayor's house, old Lempki stood at his gate. "Well, how did you survive through the night with the little one?" he asked.

"Oh, fairly well, once we had them settled down, but early this morning, the one could hardly wait till the other was fed."

"Well, did you give him a name yet?" asked Lempki. "You know it needs to be recorded in the mayor's book."

"Yes. His name is Johann," replied Isaac, twitching his cheek as he proceeded onward.

As Isaac arrived at Mayor Peters' house, he stomped his muddy shoes before knocking on the door. The air was raw and damp. The cattle had tramped through the street only a little earlier, churning up mud in the street. Far overhead, the wild geese were honking as they headed north, promising warmer and drier weather.

"Good morning," Mrs. Peters greeted him. "Now, how are things going? Did you get any sleep last night? Perhaps you slept more than we did, since I kept awakening every half hour, thinking of this mixed predicament. I sure hope everything will work out well. Once during the night, my husband remarked that this is the hardest, heartrending happening in all his twenty-one years in office.

"Is Sara able to satisfy both of the babies?"

"Yes, and she also has more work, but she feels that it's a blessing, caring for the forsaken child.

"Actually, I came here to see if Mayor Peters would have anyone in mind who might have extra baby gowns or blankets. At present, we have nothing extra with our family of seven children, but we'll make out somehow."

"I'm sorry to say that my husband left early on business, going to the Schönfeld settlement," said Susanna Peters. "He should be back before noon, but you know the roads are still soft and muddy. It's hard work for one horse, pulling the wagon."

Pfeffer, the brown shaggy dog, scratched on the door. His watchful eyes examined Isaac carefully. He slept outside the door, sounding a shrill bark if there was any unusual disturbance.

"You know, Ike, I feel that if Sara feeds the infant, the other village folks will surely share some clothing. The mayor will see to it that you get some, I'm sure. Just use what you have for now."

The mayor's dwelling did not appear to be more modern than the rest of the houses. It had only a few windows, and no indoor plumbing. Outside were a hand water pump and an outhouse. They had no money to live like a king and queen.

Susanna offered Isaac a seat on the wooden slab bench and asked, "Have you decided on a name for the little one? As you know, in three days it needs to be recorded here in the record book."

"Yes, Johann is his name."

"But what about the last name? You don't plan to keep the boy, so it won't be proper to name him Johann Harder. Should we name him Johann Derksen if John and Marie are not the true parents? I assume that we will be confronted with many more difficult decisions unless we find out who the real mother is."

"Yes, that's true," Isaac Harder replied earnestly. "I sure hope our village will not become divided through this case. This is a very unusual happening, and I certainly hope that if it creates a problem, this cruel act will be a warning to all the young girls or women throughout the whole community. We must remind our teenagers and youth that this was very ungodly.

"Even last evening at the meeting here, someone was bold enough to speak up and say that if Marie Derksen would have been smart enough to think that she couldn't nurse it, she should have just left it lying in the hog pen. No one would have ever known if the hogs ate it."

Isaac cleared his throat with a deep sigh and added, "He even had the nerve yet to say that Marie could still toss the little one back into the hog pen. Surely there are a few wicked persons who have sneaked into our village and live among us."

Susanna was quite shook up, hearing these words. "My

husband told me this morning that he has a clue that the would-be baby killer might be the fellow who hangs around in the tavern over on the other side of the hill, drinking with those Russian soldiers who have no cares about human souls. They talk filthy and foul language."

"Well, I must be going," said Isaac.

"I'll tell my husband that you were here and that Johann is the baby's name, and he'll write him in as Johann Derksen. You keep us informed about the foundling."

As Isaac left, a mid-morning wind was ruffling the new tiny leaves on the aged oak trees. Isaac took off his coat as the sun warmed up the soft trodden street.

In the next minute, Isaac met Frances Dyck. She had seen him leave the mayor's house. The stern look in her eyes told him something. Isaac bade her "Good morning," but received no response of friendship. Since people knew her as a troublemaker, he was glad that she did not start a conversation.

Frances entered Mrs. Peters' house without knocking and waiting for a "Welcome" call. She sat on the wooden plank fastened to the wall and asked in a gruff voice, "Well, Susanna, what for business did Mr. Harder have here if your husband is not here, or is he around? I assume they're already disgusted that they have committed themselves to caring for that hog-food child."

Then she saw Pfeffer the watchdog get up. He looked at her with his savage eyes. Frances feared him.

"Oh no," cried Susanna. "If it takes more of their time to care for the second baby, they do not harbor ill feelings toward the child's mother or John Derksens. They feel they are caring for a little angel sent from heaven.

"Furthermore, they know and we all know that it is not right to neglect an innocent little baby. If this would be your little grandchild, would you not be willing to help care for it? Surely you would, if you are a member of a Christian congregation. Consider your thoughts!

"Actually, Mr. Harder was here asking if we might know of anyone in this poor village who would have any extra baby nighties or blankets."

"Yes, see, I told you," snapped Frances. "They are too poor

to even buy bedding. He's liable to freeze in that drafty house unless we get warm weather soon.

"If Sara Harder does not have enough clothes for another child, she has no business trying to ask other poor folks for assistance. We'll see what becomes of that child."

Susanna could no longer control herself and broke down, crying. Pfeffer jumped up and stood in front of Frances, growling and showing his upper teeth as if to say, "I am master of this house." Frances didn't trust herself to move or take her eyes off him.

In her rage, Susanna Peters grabbed the broom from behind the stove and began sweeping the wooden kitchen floor. She had not swept since the meeting last night, and villagers had tracked a lot of dirt and sand into the house.

To keep the dust settled, she always dipped her broom into a bucket of water or poured some on the floor if it became very dusty. But now she decided to make the dust fly, to get this harsh-minded woman out of her house.

The big mouth of Frances Dyck yelled, "Pour some water on the floor! Such a dust! We'll suffocate in here." She pulled her apron to her nose and mouth.

This is just what Susanna wanted, and she swept furiously, not caring how dusty her furniture and dishes became.

Frances could not tolerate this any longer. "I'm getting out of this filthy house. It sure is not clean enough for a mayor to live in. Worse than a hog pen." As she left, she slammed the door with a terrible bang.

The mayor's wife had a keen sense that this woman knew something about the mysterious case of the abandoned baby. She was the first person to talk in opposition of Isaac and Sara's kindness.

She promptly opened the windows and doors to let the fresh air blow through the house, then took a wet rag and began cleaning away the dust everywhere. The dust had even sifted into the closet. She hung the clothes outside to let the wind blow them clean.

Soon she noticed that dust had totally covered the bowl of cream, a high-priced and scarce item. "Oh my! My precious cream is spoiled." She nearly cried as she tried to skim the dust off the cream.

Before noontime, Mayor Peters arrived home and saw the door and windows wide open. As he tied his big black horse in the barn, he was wondering what had happened.

Ascending the porch steps before entering the cold-looking kitchen, he called, "Susanna, are you in there?"

"Yes, come on in." Susanna told her husband about the offending visitor. "Frances Dyck always has bad things to say about the village folks, you know. She talked so rude about Sara and Marie: 'Why are they so concerned about this little baby if they don't have any idea to whom it belongs?' She called it silly.

"My bowl of cream is covered with dust, and I suppose we will have to feed some of it to the hog. I have a feeling that Frances is often out in the far-off pasture, talking and doing who knows what with the village herdsman. I think those two are involved in this mystery and know who dropped the infant into the hog pen."

"Well, if too many women are involved in this affair, I prefer to resign as the mayor," declared Mr. Peters. "Next time Frances comes complaining about our folks, let Pfeffer show his authority. She won't come in here again, I dare say."

ଓ 6 ଛ

"If I Ever Get Hold of That Child"

The dormant-in-winter flowers became alive under the cold earth, peeping their tiny heads upward toward the warm May sunshine. This brought a more pleasant atmosphere to the Mennonite village of Heuboden in southern Russia.

The villagers were true Christians and wanted to live in harmony, according to God's will. They did not believe in fighting in wars or in any kind of murder. The peaceful village was a close-knit church. The mayor was of the same social class as the villagers and kept close track of all the newborns. They depended on him for Christian guidance and to help protect them from any evil disturbances.

The little infant at the Isaac Harder home was getting good nourishment from his foster mother. He was gaining well, and the other children gave him loving attention. Everyone thought that the village had handled the mystery well. The stress of this unusual happening subsided.

Marie Derksen was happy again, singing as she went about her housework and planting the garden. "Next spring," she thought, "we'll have little Johann here with me, toddling along." She prayed quietly: "Please God, don't allow any harm to fall upon him. Thank you for hearing our pleading, earnest cry to have a child."

She thought of Hannah, in the Bible story, how she prayed for a son, and that she promised God to raise him to be a true servant throughout his life.

Among the three neighboring villages, John and Marie were the only married folks who had no children, so they actually had no one who understood their lonely grief. She now determined to raise this foster son to obey the teachings of Jesus.

Singing as she planted tiny seeds in the little garden, Marie felt the love of Jesus. She could hardly wait to care for the little boy, and she wished to do something for him when he was only four weeks old. She knew that the baby would need clothing.

"Yes, I'm going to sew a few pieces of clothing. But what will I use? I have no fabric of any kind in my house, and no extra money to buy any."

After lengthy thought, she decided to pick apart one of her own dresses. Then she would be able to make a tiny dress, and from the rest, a nightie, plus a few diapers. She took every precaution so as not to waste any of the faded purple dress.

"This will surely please Sara, if she need not sew for an extra child," she was thinking—when suddenly the door opened, without any sound of a knock. To her fearful surprise, Frances Dyck entered.

"I thought I'd stop in a bit on my way, since I'm going out on the hillside with Mark for a while today. He gets lonely. So you folks now are rid of that tiny bit of swine feed," she remarked, referring to the foundling.

This nasty, cruel remark caused Marie to drop her sewing project. She was stunned and could not utter one word as Frances came nearer to her.

"Well, what are you sewing? Baby clothes? You have no children," she snapped.

"I decided to practice sewing a few garments for the baby that Sara Harder is nursing. I know she has more work than she can handle."

"No, no, let Sara care for that filthy forsaken child. Let her learn the hard way. Maybe she'll get rid of it." Frances seated herself on a chair.

Marie's heart was crushed. With woe and tears, she looked out the window and spied a robin among the new leaves of the big maple tree. Its singing helped to ease her pain. She thought: "My, what a cheerful life the pretty little birds have. No hate and jealousy. They eat whatever they find and care for their young fledglings. They do not kill or steal from those who hate them."

She tried to quench her tears of self-pity as she thought of the birds. Marie kept her gaze out to the birds so Frances would not see her tears. She only wanted to get away from this sarcastic woman and decided to crawl out the window. Marie did not want to head for the door because Frances was bound to mock her for crying.

At that moment John opened the door, carrying a pail of water. Seeing Frances, he asked, "Is your husband working at Reimers today?"

"No, he went with Mayor Peters to the Schönfeld settlement. Whatever he wants there is none of your business."

John now fully realized that Frances was trying to create trouble. This was Marie's chance to get away from her. She went outside, behind the house, where she could hear the many sweetly singing birds among the trees in the orchard.

The music was such a healing balm to her grieving soul. She longed to be a cheerful mother, not a target for someone to condemn and batter down. The red-breasted bird chirped and hopped around only a few yards away from Marie, as if asking, "What is your problem? God will provide for you the same as he does for all of us birds."

As the robin flew to a low branch in the tree beside her, she heard it sing as though to say, "Put your trust in Jesus, and he will care for you."

Immediately a flock of spring birds alighted on the tree above her. They sang in high tone. She thought of the heavenly host of angels singing to the shepherds, the night Jesus was born. In a moment they all flew out of the tree, and Marie felt her entire body calm and relaxed again. "Yes," she thought, "the singing of the birds is also God's message to humans. It heals us if we listen."

As she lifted the latch of the kitchen door, she heard Frances' voice again. "I was at the mayor's house, and she was sweeping, creating a terrible dust. It sure is not fit for folks to gather for meetings in such an untidy house. See, my cloak is still dusty," she said as she laughed mockingly.

"Yes, well, I must go. I have more business to attend to yet today. I wonder where Mark is herding today."

With all this babbling, John was also becoming suspicious that Mark might know something of the foundling. Frances was not a prominent church member, and her unfavorable talk about the infant tattled on her.

After Frances left the Derksen home, Marie asked John, "What do you think of her?"

"Let her think what she wants," replied John. "We won't share anything of this situation with her. She will make an evil story out of whatever she wants. She always makes a big fuss out of not much.

"I just don't like such women. She goes around looking for trouble and then wants to be the first one to tell others. It would be much better if she stayed at home to work, sing, and pray. She pretends to be a well-known lady, but doing what she does, she gains little respect from honest folks."

Again they sat at the table to eat. The day was cloudy and overcast; so were their hearts. They carried a heavy burden of trying to do what some called foolish.

That afternoon as Marie sewed at the little gown, she decided to sing. With a low and humble voice, she kept singing as she sewed. Eventually sunlight coming through the window reflected on her lap.

As the evening shadows lengthened, John waited for the cows to come through the village. Sure enough, the herdsman came along a little earlier.

Mark squinted his nose as he sneered at John. "Now, what do you think of this?" he shouted. "Does this suit you better at seven o'clock than at eight? In Heuboden, the cows come in early to suit fussy folks who pretend to be perfect Christians."

John sure didn't like his attitude. He sensed that since the meeting in which the villagers had decided to let them have the abandoned baby, Mark hated him more than ever.

Marie milked the cow and set the milk bucket in the cool water. Tomorrow the rich cream would be on top of the milk so she could skim it off. This cream from the one cow provided a little cash for their daily income.

Three weeks later the grass was growing well, providing more milk for the village folks. The spring rains were blessings from the Lord.

"I'm going over to Harders this evening," Marie called to John as he left the barn. "I don't want to stay alone in the house after dark since Frances was here again. Neither do I trust Mark, but I do feel assurances that God will not let any harm fall on us."

Before she left for the Harder dwelling, Marie decided to close the shutters of the three windows in the house. As she closed the one on the back side, she heard a voice from the distance: "If I ever get hold of that child, that will be the end of it."

She drew her shoulders together and shivered. In that very moment, she ran into the house, grabbed her mantle, locked the door, and ran off to the stables. "John, John, where are you?" she puffed excitedly, nearly collapsing. John had already left, and she could not find him.

As the sun set beyond the horizon, the streaks of reddish and yellow hues soothed her weary body only a wee bit. She cried to herself as she fled the barnyard, going back beyond the wooden fence. A few trees grew along the village boundary line. She did not feel safe walking the front street or the back lane but ran out through the open fields.

Soon she saw an old couple, the Wiebes. Mrs. Wiebe saw Marie running toward them. "My land!" she exclaimed. "What is all your excitement about? Is it about the baby again? Surely Sara Harder is protecting it as well as any mother far around."

"Yes and no," replied Marie. "I am just so confused and afraid to stay alone, even in broad daylight." Her whole body trembled as she cried in anguish, asking, "Have you seen anything of John? Where do Isaac Harders live? I just can't think."

She told them what she had just experienced. They feared the worst, the same as Marie. Old Mr. Wiebe said, "Something must be done about this. I'll go and see the mayor as soon as we are done with this last load of hedge hay." They pointed out the direction to the Harders, and off she ran.

Old folks like the Wiebes tried to gather what they could find for their few animals. In season they clipped off hedge bushes for hay. They sickled off dried grass and put it on piles inside their small barn. Only a few folks had a farm wagon, and so they carried the cuttings in by hand, a big armful at a time.

Inside their barn, Mr. Wiebe noticed that someone had made what looked like a soft bed of hay. "Who would have slept in my barn last night?" he mused to himself. "This looks suspicious. It is quite a mystery. Something is happening in our peaceful village, and rumors are going every way. We must put a stop to it."

He looked closely at the pile of dried and shaggy hay to see if he could find any trace of mischief. "For all I know, it might have been the shepherd or perhaps someone's dog," Mr. Wiebe told his wife. "But we must be careful not to say anything about whatever laid in our hay pile. It is not right to criticize anyone if we are not sure. We are not true followers of Christ if we misjudge anyone, including neighbors."

At twilight John Derksen walked past Isaac Harder's house. Marie saw him and immediately ran out. "John," she screamed, "I could hardly wait till you came back home again." Marie told her husband what she had just experienced. "John, I'm afraid something will happen to our baby yet. Oh, the dear soul!"

She sobbed upon John's breast. He wrapped his strong, steady arms around her as he silently prayed to God and recited Psalm 23: "The Lord is my shepherd; I shall not want. . . . Thy rod and thy staff, they comfort me."

Amid her sobs, Marie thought, "Will he? Yes, God *will* protect us. I do not question that."

Again she felt the comfort of the almighty God. She trusted the psalmist's words and looked into the moist blue eyes of her good husband, thinking, "Thank God for John's calm nature and understanding ways during these heartrending trials." Marie knew she could trust God and also her beloved husband.

As the morning dawned and the crimson red sun rose in late May, everything seemed to be going quite smoothly. From the green leafy branches, the summer birds echoed their sweet music. The few wild flowers that grew along the garden fences and village streets bloomed. Little children picked a few to give to their mothers. The villagers tended every garden quite well, and vegetables thrived abundantly. Every mother tried her very best to raise enough food for her family.

Marie went over to Isaac's every few days to see her baby. As the two babies lay in the same bed one morning, Marie was watching them. Her head hung toward her right shoulder. She was happy and smiling again as Isaac said, "Well, Marie, which one of the two looks the healthiest?"

"Oh, they're both healthy, and I think the darlings look much alike." Marie replied. "But anyone can see that they're not twins."

"We weighed them again yesterday, and they are nearly the same weight," reported Isaac.

"I just knew Aunt Sara would be a good mother to baby Johann," Marie said.

That noon Sara asked her to stay for dinner. She boiled coffee made of roasted grain and also cooked milk and sliced small pieces of bread into the pot, for bread soup. There were no fancy foods. They were merely content with most anything. During the summer months, their fuel for cooking was mostly straw and mulberry twigs.

After supper, John said, "I'd like to go to Ike's this evening to see the baby again. What do you say?"

"Sure, it's never too often for me, even though I was there this morning and Sara asked me to stay for dinner."

John felt awkward while holding a baby, but he dearly loved the precious infant. He fussed and talked to Johann, trying to bring a tiny smile to his face.

Marie was holding Sara's baby Jacob. "Wouldn't this be great if we could have both of them? We never actually realized what we were missing by not having children."

"Let's not become greedy, Marie. In our prayer, we promised God that we would be well satisfied if we could have only one child. Remember that.

"Oh, look, Marie. He's smiling at me. Oh, isn't he cute?"

Soon both babies fell asleep, and John and Marie left for home. They were so happy but did not trust talking louder than a whisper, fearing someone might hear them on the street.

In the intense darkness, as they approached their yard gate, suddenly they both made out the figure of a woman stealing around the corner of the barn. At once she was lost in the darkness. Marie took hold of John's hand and nearly screamed. "Who could be snooping around our house on a dark and moonless night?" she whispered to him.

Inside the kitchen, they first did not even trust lighting their candle, made of flax thread coated with wax and tallow. Marie sat down. She felt as though she was fainting. "Is someone still after our baby?" she cried. "Why must we be so torn between love and fear for the sweet, innocent child?" she grieved. "My whole body was so relaxed this evening at Ike's. Now I feel like crying. John, I can't take any more of this."

She lit the candle, and they both fell onto bended knees as John read from the German prayer book. Marie snuggled tightly against her brave husband to gain control of her shattered nerves.

The childless couple crawled into their bed, trusting that God would protect their foster child from any evil.

❧ 7 ❧

Trashed Again

In the week of Ascension Day, the school doors were closed. The seven-month year was over. During the term, the oldest pupils were free to attend when it suited best. Sara Harder was glad to have more help from her girls in caring for the two babies.

Isaac was a more progressive farmer than most of the folks. He had a fairly large barn, which stabled three horses and four cows. The villagers' barns were all on one level, with no second floor. All the hog pens were on the back side of the barn, and they let the hogs outside, to root in the dirt inside a rail fence. The farmers also kept hay, straw, and corn in their barns.

These Russian Mennonites of the 1860s sincerely celebrated their religious holidays. On a Thursday forty days after Easter, they observed Ascension Day, when Jesus ascended to heaven. Then ten days later, they took three days to celebrate Pentecost.

On Pentecost Sunday, they deemed it wise to baptize their boys and girls who were well into the stage of puberty and could give their assent to the faith. Some of the parents had minor disputes because they wanted the preacher to baptize their youth in a stream, more like Jesus was baptized.

A few days after Pentecost, Isaac was in the barn, cleaning and sweeping, getting ready to haul hay into the far side of the barn. He owned a heavy two-horse sleigh and one farm wagon. As he pushed the wooden-wheeled wagon to sweep underneath it, the heavy tongue slipped out of his hands, creating a loud noise.

"Isaac! Isaac!" came a tremendous shrill voice from the horse stable. "Come here right now," yelled Sara. "Our little baby is lying at the hind feet of the big sorrel horse."

Isaac knew something terrible must have happened since Sara had never yelled like this before. She was always very calm.

As Isaac turned to run, he stumbled over the wagon tongue and fell upon his left arm. "Ouch! Oh, my arm!" he screamed in awful pain. He quickly got on his feet again and ran. He had not understood what Sara had screamed about the baby.

"Get the little baby away from the horse's feet," yelled Sara. "Oh, Isaac, I'm afraid Scott will tramp on him. Please, see, Scott is ready to step on him."

Isaac didn't know what she meant since she had a baby in her arms. "Where do you mean?" he asked, and then he looked at Scott. "Whoa, easy, Scott," he soothed the huge beast as he reached to grab the baby out of the horse manure.

The big chunky horse was calm, not realizing what all the commotion meant. With all his weight, if he would have stepped on the little creature, he would have smashed it.

Sara kept a tight hold of her little Jacob, crying, "I can't take this any more. How shall I protect this darling from the murderer stalking our neighborhood?"

Ike cradled the infant in his brawny arms, speaking softly to his wife as the baby began crying. Baby Johann had been lying face down, and filthy horse manure coated his face and gown. He looked awful.

"We need to get inside the house to figure out this situation," Isaac said. "We definitely need help. This is getting the best of me too."

As the couple entered the kitchen with the two babies, Isaac finally gathered his senses and asked, "How did baby Johann get out in the horse stable? I thought the children are all in the far end of the field, hoeing weeds in the corn."

"Yes," replied Sara. "I had just finished feeding Jacob ten minutes earlier and had gone out to the garden. I thought that both babies were sound asleep. As I came back to get a hoe out of the shanty, I thought I'd check on the little ones again. Johann was missing. I guess I am always tense and fearful of leaving them alone in the house. I could hardly ever forgive myself if something happened to Marie's baby.

"I simply panicked, picked up Jacob, and ran to tell you. As I ran by the horse stable, there lay a baby right at Scott's hind feet."

She flopped into a chair. "I just could not believe my own eyes. It looked horrible. I figured that he was dead."

They both checked the kitchen and the two bedrooms for any

trace that might show who had been in the house. They detected nothing unusual. The parents were glad that none of their children needed to see this.

"I think I know most certainly what's happening around here," said Isaac. "But why does no one have any clues as to who might be doing these awful things? This is so stressful, and yet we offered to care for the baby, to help John and Marie."

As Sara began cleaning Johann's scummy face with a warm washcloth, she burst out crying. Her heart was so hurt. She bathed him thoroughly and dressed the precious boy in a clean gown, cuddled him upon her breast, and kissed him.

"Oh, you sweet innocent child, you truly are not aware of the enemy in your young life. I trust and pray that you will not have to endure this any longer. No way do you or any of us deserve this."

Isaac and Sara sat there quite a while in deep thoughts, each holding a baby. They were puzzled. A tiny doubt entered Sara's mind, and she asked her husband: "Should we not have offered to nurse and care for this child?"

"No, Sara. It's not right to regret any good deeds anyone has ever offered. Satan is the one who sets such thoughts in people's hearts. We will get help and strength to endure this trial. I think it's best that I go and tell Mayor Peters. Let's see what he can suggest."

"I don't want to stay alone with both babies," Sara said.

Isaac looked at the mantel clock. "The children should soon come in from the field. I hope to be back before dinner."

In the stable he checked to see if he could detect anything different. "Nothing! Simply a mystery. How did all this happen in the few moments that Sara was in the garden?" he asked himself.

Scott looked around to his master, not realizing what had happened. He was much more content than Isaac. "Why do we have a fear of our own nature?" thought Isaac. "The animals get along better than humans do."

While the two infants were asleep again, Sara locked the door, took the family Bible out of the cupboard, and paged to Daniel, chapter 6. She found condolence and peace in her heart as she read how an angel saved Daniel from the lions' mouths. Sara firmly believed that God would spare the life of Marie's baby.

Isaac fed the two horses and walked down the street to see Mayor Peters. He met the mayor in the driveway, hitching his horse to the buggy for another journey to Schönfeld, the next settlement. Isaac greeted Mr. Peters but did not know how to start his subject. He half expected the mayor to think, "Why are you always having problems?"

"Well, what happened now? I can see that something's wrong."

This eased the pressure and let Isaac know that Mr. Peters cared. "Yes, something terrible happened less than an hour ago. We can hardly handle this mess any longer. Sara found the foster son at the feet of our big sorrel horse."

The mayor tied his horse to the hitching post. "Isaac, come on inside with me so that my wife is a witness to what you say. This sounds serious."

As the three sat in the mayor's office, with carved designs above the only window and door, Isaac related the unusual incident. Mrs. Peters hung her head into her left hand, in deep thoughts: "Could this really be true? Is Isaac telling a false story to trap someone? If this keeps on, the peace in our village will be gone. We must get ahead of this somehow."

Susanna looked out the window. Everyone was quiet. She burst into sobs, thinking, "What if this were my child?" Tears rolled off her crumpled cheeks onto her dark-blue apron.

"How will this ever end?" she asked. "Oh, I don't like these gruesome things."

Isaac wept too.

Susanna suggested, "Why don't we get watchmen or scouts to guard their premises?"

"That's good advice," said Mr. Peters. "What do you think of the idea, Ike? We must do something."

"I'm ready to give it a try, and yet we do not want to give up relying on a higher hand," replied Isaac.

"I'll ask Thiessen and Wiebe to watch tonight, and Froese and Rempel for tomorrow night. Maybe other men are willing to offer their help other nights. But what about during the day? You know that what happened today was in broad daylight.

"I'll ask some advice about this when I get to Schönfeld.

Maybe someone has a clue to this mystery. It could be that some woman is missing in another village and might be creating trouble for us. I'll check it out."

Mayor Peters left for Schönfeld. As Isaac was about to leave, Mrs. Peters gave him some meat and apples to help them conquer their stress.

"Oh, thank you," responded Isaac. "I see that we got more than we bargained for. We meant it as good to help in caring for the forsaken child. Now we need your prayers to keep going.

"You know, Susanna, I often wonder if the person who threw the baby in the hog pen was watching somewhere close by, to have evidence that the big sow ate the child. Could it be that she saw Marie pick up the baby? Also, someone might have been at the extra village meeting as a spy to find out what was decided about the foundling.

"Someday, yes, someday the Lord will punish the people involved in this evil act. They will suffer much, much more by carrying a guilty conscience, wishing they had never done it. The Lord does not let a troubled mind rest. We all know that.

"But I have hay to haul in today, so I must go. Thanks for your kindness. It's just good to talk to someone. So long."

"Good-bye, Isaac. I'll see that my husband has sentinels out tonight."

As Ike was walking through his yard, Marie greeted him. "Hello, Isaac. It sure is a nice day. I suppose you are about to start hauling hay, or did you finish last evening? Where are the children? Everything is quiet. Are they out in the garden helping Sara?

"I asked John to come with me so he could help you today, but he had promised Abram Boerg in Schönfeld to help put up hay. He left early."

Isaac tried to stay calm but thought that it was best for him rather than his wife to tell Marie of the latest incident. Sara seemed almost at the point of a nervous breakdown.

"Well, Marie, we've experienced another terrible scene this forenoon. Sara found baby Johann's cradle empty, and as she ran to tell me, she saw him lying by Scott's hind feet. We rescued your baby, and he's okay. Sara's nerves are bad, so try to remain calm in her presence if at all possible. We will not make much fuss about it to our children. Next thing they will get scared."

Marie gasped for breath as she heard these shocking words. She could not talk but sobbed as she headed for the house. Marie felt sick and more confused than ever, thinking, "Must every nice morning turn into sorrow later in the day?"

Sara fidgeted and jumped as the door opened. As she saw Marie, she greeted her with sobs. The two women clasped their arms around each other. They cried and cried.

"Marie, Marie, how terrible! Could you believe—" She could not go on.

Between sobs, Marie said, "Yes, Isaac told me outside."

Warm tears wetted each other's shoulders. Finally they walked to the two cradles. Both babies were sleeping so innocently.

"Sit down, Marie. I know how you feel. I had no idea anyone was around when I was in the garden. Someone is watching our house, trying to harm your child. I hope you can forgive me for not staying inside. I promise not to go out of sight again."

"No, Sara, no. I do not blame you at all," Marie assured her as she dried her eyes with her green handkerchief. "I've known your gracious, good heart all my life. You are just like a mother to me. I know this child is like a grandchild to you."

Marie burst out crying again. "Are we just not supposed to have children? Oh, I can't take this. I wish I'd never seen—" She could not finish these words.

"How come it was not your baby? How did this person know which is mine or, shall I say, her baby? I dare say it's Johann's mother who is causing this trouble. If she wants him, why doesn't she take him to her home? No one else would have known which baby belongs to you or me."

The steel latch on the unfinished door clicked. Since they were so nervous, both women's bodies twitched.

Isaac stepped inside. "Are the babies sleeping? Marie, I feel so sorry for you, and yet it hurts us the same as it does you. I hardly know how to comfort you. Before I left, Mrs. Peters said that she will make sure that the mayor will have watchmen out tonight, to protect the baby and us."

After their tears subsided, all three sat in deep silence. Finally in submission to God, they shared their thoughts.

"As long as this child is alive, we will support you folks," promised Isaac, "no matter what."

"Well," said Marie, "if anyone in this village thinks we should not have Johann as our own, I am ready to obey and give up the child. This is wearing down my body, and I am not sure if it's worth it. Someone else may take him, or else you folks may keep him forever. Maybe God has other children planned for us."

"No, Marie, I still think you are to be his mother," Sara assured her. "I had a dream of you and the dear child on Wednesday night. It was his first day of school, and I saw you standing at the gate, waving good-bye. Your precious son turned to wave at you, with a big smile on his tanned and healthy-looking face. He was carrying his lunch basket in the other hand.

"In the days of the prophets, dreams came true. The people believed their dreams when God spoke to them. Let us believe this dream and hope it will come true."

Isaac went to the water bucket, took a drink, and said, "Well, I must get started with my hay."

Before he went out the door, he remarked, "If this peaceful village is no longer safe for infants, we may think of moving to another one. But moving away from problems is not always the answer. Many folks have discovered that in their lifetime."

Sara invited Marie to stay for dinner. Soon they heard the Harder children romping though the yard. They knew nothing of the episode that had occurred. "The innocent children need not know all the heartaches and sorrows of older folks," Sara thought.

Using only a few words, she told the youngsters about the happening, then added, "Now please be quiet. Don't ask any questions. Someday you may understand."

Marie stood by the cradle, looking at her infant. Her thoughts rolled to the past and also to the future.

Peter, the four-year-old Harder boy, went to check on the babies. He noticed the sad face of Marie as she stood at the bed of baby Johann. No words were spoken. He glanced at the baby, then went to the other cradle, and finally looked at Marie again before he went back to the kitchen. The poor boy could not understand.

The pesky flies sat on the sleeping little faces. Marie waved them off. They ate the noon meal in near silence. After dinner, Marie walked the back lane to her home. When her husband came home after supper, she told him of the near tragedy.

Before darkness fell upon the quiet Mennonite village, Mayor Peters dispatched watchmen. Thiessen was at the back lane behind the Harders, and Wiebe at the front gate. His big brown dog lay at his feet. Any noise during the night would alarm him.

Occasionally the two men spoke a few words to be sure that the other was not sleeping. This was a totally new practice for these peace-loving folks. At midnight two other men traded places with them. They owned no weapons, but their keen eyes and ears were scanning the Harder plot.

The crescent moon set in the west. The village was dark and quiet, with stars sparkling in the night sky. They kept up this watch for a few weeks. Nothing unusual happened except for a few roosters crowing in the late night hours. The village slumbered in peace.

Perhaps the culprit gave up trying to do harm to the infant. The village folks began to relax more again, but Sara always kept a close check on baby Johann. She was determined to fulfill her true love to her niece Marie and her baby.

Surely many of you readers will think, "Why would a mother want to kill her own baby?" Anyone with a sound mind knows that it is a sin to kill people. Doing so creates a guilty conscience, the same as it did for Cain, who killed his only brother, as Genesis tells us. God's punishment for Cain was for him to be a fugitive and vagabond on the earth. Cain admitted, "My punishment is greater than I can bear."

A few weeks passed by, a month, and years, and nothing untoward happened regarding the baby Johann. The village of Heuboden enjoyed peace and quiet again.

We will turn from the heartaches of John and Marie for a while, until the little boy starts to school. He has yet to face some hard things in his life. Meanwhile, let us go back a few years to see where this innocent child was born.

☙ 8 ❧

"Does the Child Live?"

It was late in the evening, and the village appeared as dead. Folks were slumbering, and the houses were dark except for one. Outside was total darkness, near new moon, with not a star appearing in the cloudy night.

At the last house of the village street, one might have seen a faint light coming through the two dirty windows. The dim shadows visible through the window showed that a few folks were hastily moving about in the small untidy kitchen. The forms kept active as the night hours crept on. What could be going on? Why weren't these old folks relaxed? They should be sound asleep.

These old folks were a bit different from most of the elderly people of Heuboden. Only a few years earlier, they had moved in from quite a distance. They were not considered Christians, and evidently some folks knew this.

On this chilly April evening, a guest had knocked on their door after twilight. It was a young woman in labor, a friend they knew. The old woman accepted her earnest plea, asking to stay for a few weeks. The girl was desperate for help and lodging. The fifty-year-old lady knew she was not honoring her conscience by giving in to this weary, burdened teenager's plan.

She showed the girl a bed. The rough-looking homeless wanderer lay down and sighed. She cried, begging the old man and woman to support her in secrecy. The old folks, native Russians, both agreed to her plan.

"No one will ever find out about it if you keep quiet," the girl said. That night she quivered, tossing about restlessly.

Shortly after midnight the cries of a newborn were heard in the house. The weary woman laid the infant on a bench by the brick stove. She covered it with a ragged, worn cover. The baby cried loudly, and she covered the tiny head so no one outside the house would hear the sounds.

After a hard birthing experience, the new mother sank into unconsciousness. An hour later she asked, "Does the child live?"

"Yes, but my husband will soon take care of it."

The sobbing young mother tried to rest on the old flat straw-tick bed. She was miserable in body and mind. The devil still had control of her. She thought of her own mother, miles away, whom she had disobeyed.

A serious thought came to her: "What if my mother ever finds out about this? What would Dad say? I am a homeless wanderer, bound by sin." She cried in desperate grief. A glimpse of God came to her grieving mind, but soon Satan overpowered her again.

Her motherly instinct burdened her. She had a longing to see her offspring, but "No! I want to be rid of it," she told herself. "I don't want to raise it by myself. Actually, don't even see how I could raise it. It's better that it dies now rather than suffer a hard life." Her final thoughts on the matter were as she had earlier planned. Sleep again overtook her weary body.

The tired old woman snapped at her drowsy husband, sitting on a broken chair by the stove. "Come on, Cornelius. Take this little bundle out and lay it in someone's yard or feed entry. Cover it up a bit. Someone will surely find it. You must go before daylight, as you promised, or we'll be in deep trouble if one living soul finds out about this."

"I'm not taking it out tonight. Didn't get any sleep yet," the old man grumbled. "Early in the morn is still time."

The big shaggy white-faced dog lay by the door, listening curiously to the sound of the covered-up whimpering baby. His mistress had ordered him to lie there, to detect any sound from the outside.

The old woman took a heavy horsehide blanket to cover the restless young mother. Her nervous body trembled.

The new mother slept a little. Suddenly she exploded in a high-pitched voice, "Ouch! Ow, oh my! What's biting me?" She sat up in her rugged bed. The blanket was infested with tiny ants, which became active from her body heat.

In the droopy kitchen stood a three-legged wooden table, and beside it was a wooden barrel partly filled with sour cabbage left from last fall. The stench reeked in her nostrils. Her stomach became upset.

Miserably she cried again: "Did you folks take care of it?"

She wished she could reverse this ungodly mess she had become involved in. But it was too late. She knew she was a sinful mother. "I am no longer a virgin." She buried her face in the stained pillow and tried to cry, but no tears came. She felt doomed and wished that her life could somehow end.

Again she asked for water. The old woman resented having to give her a drink, possibly the sixth time in the past four hours.

Cornelius was snoring as he awoke to the growl of his wife: "Now you take this little one out right now, before daybreak. Do you hear?"

The baby had not uttered a sound the last two hours. The old folks hoped it hadn't smothered under the heavy blanket.

The others had finally fallen into a deep sleep. As streaks of red arose in the east, something aroused the old woman. She removed the cover from the tiny figure, which whimpered and then began crying. "Oh, you little worm, I thought you were sleeping," she snarled.

Cornelius awoke to his wife's screams. "You get your coat and take this thing outside right now. I tied a cloth around its neck, so it can't cry loud while you are walking the street."

The young mother heard these words. "Now my wicked plans are being fulfilled," she thought. But she could not rest. It was not that easy. Her mind wandered back to different stages of her early teenage years and warnings she had heard: "Do not play with sin. Be sure your sin will find you out."

"Mother will never find out about this, I'm sure," she murmured to herself. "I'll go back home someday and be a good Christian girl. Mother often reminded us girls that if we ask Jesus for forgiveness, he will forgive us. Now if these plans work out, my life should go smoothly again."

But she had not realized how tight a grip Satan had on her. Every day she thought she would break away from her downward track, but she could not. Satan was stronger than she was. She carried a terrible guilt.

☙ 9 ❧

"Did They Find That Baby?"

At dawn the temperature was at the freezing point. The village began to stir.

An old man was walking the dirty back lane, carrying a small bundle on a stick flung over his shoulder, as though he was going on an errand. He had planned to take the bundle along the alley somewhere, as his wife had told him.

As he passed by Reimer's hog pen, he stopped, and with confused thoughts, he stepped closer. He wondered if this might not be a good place to get rid of this bundle. In a moment he swung his stick around, and the pack landed in the sticky hog manure.

"This is easier than getting caught carrying it," he mumbled to himself. "It wasn't my plan to have this baby in our house. This way, no dog will find it and drag it around. Then the rumors would rage like a fire. This is good sow feed," he said with a sober chuckle.

At this moment Cornelius heard the sound of a door closing. Slowly he turned toward the noise and saw a young woman approaching the corner of the back barnyard alley, only two hundred feet away. He sensed that she did not notice anyone, so he quickly slipped into the side feed entry and passed through to the front street.

As he walked toward his home, it was becoming broad daylight. Relieved of the night's trouble, he stepped into the kitchen. The dog growled and showed his teeth. Did he sense what his master had done?

"Shut up, you big mutt. What ails you? Lie down."

"You're back already?" the old lady grilled her husband. "Where did you put it?"

At this moment the young woman sat up in her bed, eyes glaring at him. She wanted to hear every word. Her nerves were throbbing in her whole body. Cornelius told them how he had found a clever place to put it: "In the hog manure. The big sow is likely having a feast by now. Nothing wrong with that. We eat hog meat, too."

At this, the new mother shivered and lamented, "Oh, my baby!" She fell back on the pillow and covered her face with her hands. This time tears of remorse wetted her hands and face as she thought of Jesus' love for the children. She sobbed in anguish. Now she was truthfully sorry, but it was too late. She simply could not bear to think of what was happening.

The old woman fumed and raged at these words from Cornelius. "Again you did not listen to what I told you."

"Don't worry. Everything is taken care of," he shot back. "I want my coffee right now. D'you hear?" He sighed in relief as his heavy body slumped onto a chair, ready for his breakfast of rye bread, milk, and coffee.

After the late noon meal, the old woman opened the door to let the dog out and heard voices of serious confusion in the distance. Looking north to where the sound came from, she saw Pete Reimer and his wife, plus a few others, at Reimer's hog yard. Their actions showed that they were excited about something.

"Cornelius, what's going on at the Reimers?"

He got up and looked out the window. "Hey, they didn't find that baby, did they? Very few people walk the back lane early in the morning. Wonder if that young woman went that way after I chucked it in. Sharp-eyed as a Peeping Tom, she must be. Sure hope the old sow wasn't munching it down in her presence. Probably what happened."

"I told you to go out last night, but you were too stubborn," scolded the straggly haired woman.

"Oh, be quiet! The child's dead anyhow. I'll go for a walk past them to see what I can find out. They'll never detect a thing."

The old lady plopped onto a chair, thinking the worst.

Cornelius soon heard the excited conversations:

"Someone found a tiny baby in the hog manure."

"Did you say it was alive?"

"Yes."

"Where is it?"

"John Derksen's wife found it and snatched it out of the slop just as the big sow was coming for it."

"Surely it must have happened only a short while earlier, or it would have been devoured or frozen if it was in there last night."

"Where is it now?"

"John's wife took it to her home," said Mr. Giesbrecht.

This was too much for Cornelius. He pretended to be alarmed also, asking a few questions as he climbed onto the fence, browsing around with a serious look on his face. Then he moved on, taking the other back lane toward home. The big dog growled again as he entered.

"Now," quizzed his wife, "what is it all about? Did they find that baby?"

He stuttered, "Y-y-yess. John Derksen's wife has it in her home, and it is still alive, but it's all your fault. You didn't tie that cloth tight enough around the neck. I heard faint cries as I walked the alley."

The young mother screamed as she heard his answer: "You lousy old critter! You promised me that you would help me out in my predicament when I came here last night. I'm gonna run off tonight. I don't want to live any more, but I have no place to go to. Oh, this is the worst hardship I've ever met in all my seventeen years on earth."

She broke down, crying in pathetic sobs. Her body was so weak that she could not sit up. She had no appetite and knew she could not run off in this condition. The only choice she had was to stay hidden. She tried to pray but couldn't.

Her mind rambled on as she told herself: "I thought I had my life all planned. I was gonna have a grand life later on. Should I repent? No, I'm involved in sin. There is no forgiveness for me. Frances Dyck will be my friend. She will help me along somehow. Someday I'll go back to my mother, but as of now, I'm not going to be a mother to a newborn child. I'll get rid of it somehow yet."

Satan still had a tremendous hold on her young life. She nicked her face with her fingernails. She was not happy.

Later in the afternoon, someone knocked on the door. The

old woman opened it only a wee bit. The visitor slipped a note through the crack and onto the floor.

"Eight o'clock meeting at Mayor Peters tonight," she huffed to her husband. "It says to pass the note on to the next house. Here, take this note. We don't want it to stall here at our house, or surely the Heuboden folks will become suspicious."

Cornelius put on his homemade coat, went out, and handed the note to the neighbor lady. She was planting a few flowers, so he didn't stay long.

Back in the untidy kitchen, he flopped on the couch. "I'm not going to the meeting tonight. I know what it's all about. I hardly got any sleep last night. You nasty women are driving me crazy."

His wife abruptly told him different: "You sure are going. We want to know what the outcome of this child will be. We need to know to protect ourselves. All three of us are at risk. Act stupid and don't say a word."

At the well-attended meeting, everyone was sad and serious minded. The question came forth: "Does anyone have any clue where or who the mother of this infant is?" The room was totally quiet: no sound.

As Mayor Peters proceeded to raise the question of what to do in this case, people threw out a few proposals. With differing mind-sets, the folks were debating possible decisions. The room became noisy again. From the talk, Cornelius detected that the child was still at John Derksen's place.

At this moment Cornelius quietly slipped out the door and headed home in haste. He went by the Derksen house and stopped there only long enough to peep in the window. He saw Marie Derksen and another woman, each holding a tiny baby on their laps.

When Cornelius reported all this at home, the young mother felt insulted, hearing that another woman was enjoying her baby. "The first chance I have to lay my hands on it, that will be the end of it."

That night the three at that house struggled to sleep. They could not rest even though they felt sure that the child was well taken care of.

Two nights and one day without any sleep tired their weary

bodies. Guilty consciences continuously bogged down their minds. They became irritated and blamed each other. In their vexation and mental turmoil, they hurled harsh words at each other.

The three sat at the table to eat. The young mother sipped her coffee of dried grains. Nothing tasted good. She was weak and exhausted.

After the fourth day, she was eating better. She slept some during the day, but at night when everything was dark and quiet, she tossed and turned, thinking, "I'm young, but already my life is ruined."

In the dark night she raved with bitter thoughts, trying to defend herself, blaming this sin on a man who tempted her. She thought of her loving mother and burst into sobs. This relieved her a bit. "I hope my dear mother is praying for me," she thought.

The dark night seemed endless as she heard the old man snoring. She went to the water bucket again and again, trying to drown her shameful thoughts.

The morning beamed its bright rays of sunshine over the rooftops of the village. She remembered that her mother and father, on bended knees, prayed every morning with their children. Here in this house, there were no prayers. Tears rolled down her cheeks as she sobbed: "God, forgive me. I'm a sinner."

She had lost memory of the prayer her mother had taught her in her childhood days. As she thought hard, finally it came back to her, at least part of it. This relieved her guilty conscience enough that she once more had a desire to go outside for fresh air. She felt stronger, but in her mind she was terribly confused.

The young mother did not trust going outside alone, so the old woman walked with her. They tried to stay among trees to keep people from noticing them.

After the evening shadows had fallen, they went outside for a daily walk. The young mother's days and nights were long and weary. She was not happy being cooped up with these old grumpy folks. By now, she wished to go to a far-off village, looking for a job and enjoying life again. But first she wanted to fulfill her plans for her little child.

Acting as a spy, the old man kept track of what he heard

among the villagers. He told the young mother these things. So she occasionally walked by the Harders' back lane.

One day she saw Mrs. Harder working in the garden. Quickly she glanced all around the property to be sure no one else was in sight. Unnoticed by the Harder woman, she ran toward her house and entered the back door. "Well, where is my little runt?" she thought. She opened a bedroom door, and there were two cradles.

"Now, here's my chance." Her mother instinct told her right away which baby belonged to her. "Yes, I have a full right to take it," she told herself. The baby's sweet face did not sway her resolve. She clamped the blanket over the entire body.

In haste she ran for the back door. As she approached that partly open door, she saw the Harder lady nearing it. In her excited fury, she looked for another way out. The front door was her only chance. Out through the stable she ran, holding the blanket in one arm and opening doors with the other.

Suddenly she heard a loud noise in the far end of the barn. In a quick decision she threw her load of trouble at the feet of the big brown workhorse. She slipped through the stable, crawled out an open window, and for a moment crouched behind the mulberry bushes there. Then she cautiously made her way back to the old couple with whom she was living.

"Okay, now it's done," she reported.

"What, is everything taken care of?" asked the old woman.

"Yes, the young one won't have a chance to survive. It's lying at the hind feet of Harder's big horse. Surely he'll trample it in a few minutes, and it will be squished in the horse manure. No one will ever find it alive.

"Oh, that sure is a relief! Now for once I can relax again and get my strength back," she said as she sighed deeply and lay down.

"Are you sure you took yours and not Harders' baby?" asked the old woman. "That could create a much bigger issue.

"I've decided that I'll never again take someone in my house like this. I sure hope I can knock off this guilty conscience soon, before my nerves collapse. This sure isn't worth it. Don't know what ails you, killing your own child. That's a bad crime."

"Yes, I know, and I also immediately knew which one was mine. Now keep quiet so I can rest," snapped the young woman.

She closed her eyes, but her scattered thoughts kept nagging her. She covered her head with the dirty gray blanket to blank out the awful sight of a tiny baby smashed by a big workhorse's feet.

At last she was so weary that sleep overtook her—but for only a little while. Bad dreams made her whole body tremble. "Oh, this is simply horrible. How long must I endure this stress," she screamed again. "I wish I could die."

The old mistress mixed a solution of herbal tea to relieve her misery and fever. Her bad nerves made her frail body quiver. For three weeks she struggled through these mental scenes of her dying baby.

"Why can't I find any relief?" she asked the old woman. "I never had such nerve problems before. Is there no doctor in this village who could help me?"

"Yes, there is old Doctor Penton, but do you want to tell him your problem?"

The young woman decided to face the fact that she had made a big mistake in her young life by not being obedient to her mother's earnest pleas: "Keep your young body pure and holy, and do not yield to sin. This will be a rewarding and happy life."

She wished to go and meet her mother and tell her about her own drastic and unsolved problem, but out of pity for her loving mother, she hesitated. She knew her mother would be honest and fair. It would hurt for the daughter to face the truth of her mother's counsel, which she had not followed. "No lying or any kind of excuses will pardon me," she told herself. "I must confess my sins someday—but when?

"I-I still love my mother," she stammered to herself, "but I dare not break her heart. I'll swallow the consequences myself and get a job in another village, somewhere. I'm not a young Mennonite girl anymore."

One day some folks with whom she was familiar met her. They quickly noticed her change to a different dress and attitude. She couldn't hide it.

As a result, she asked herself, "Why must I still feel guilty every time I meet someone familiar? Surely if my baby is in heaven, it is safe from all harm. But what about me? I'll hardly make it."

Dear readers: Why did King Saul, the anointed of God, try a few times to destroy the rising leader David, who was also one of God's chosen people? Was it not jealousness?

We are now living in the days of the New Testament, when Jesus will forgive our sins if we accept his teaching. But Jesus still reminds us of the Ten Commandments: "Thou shalt not kill."

ଔ 10 ଓ

With the Derksens

Sara Harder was kept busy with the two babies. Every few days Marie came walking by. With a delightful heart, she bathed her little sweetheart. He smiled and cooed to both women, adding a healthy bit of sunshine to their hearts. Baby Johann was eating well and was nearly a year old.

By then he was totally weaned from nursing. Harders and Derksens decided that it was time for him to live with John and Marie. Johns were so happy. Now there were three in their family.

As the baby sat at the table on the high chair, they taught him to keep his tiny hands down while saying grace. Their true and affectionate love prompted the child to listen and obey willingly. Baby Johann slept in a little bed.

In their morning and evening prayers, the Derksens always asked that God would protect their child from any harm. Marie trusted that Frances Dyck would not create any more problems if little Johann was in their house.

"But what about the birth mother?" she thought. "Did she forget about her baby by now?"

In the fall of 1863, the cold wind blew through the bare trees of the Heuboden village. The crops and food were stored, ready for winter. Everyone hoped to have enough heating supplies to stay fairly warm.

One evening John and Marie Derksen had invited a few friends for supper. As Marie prepared the table, little Johann was sitting on his high chair. He screamed and pulled at the tablecloth.

"Oh my, your little one is hungry and full of pep," said Sara Harder. "Who knows what all he must see or what his life will be when he grows up? He might become rich, or he might be a useful servant someday. Only God knows."

At this moment she noticed a figure in the darkness outside the kitchen window. Since they had no curtains, their only protection from a Peeping Tom was to open the window and reach out to close the unpainted shutters. But the women were afraid to open the window.

Marie shivered at the thought of someone outside watching or listening. She went to the cupboard to get some bread and also to wipe off her tears. When she returned, she told Sara, "There's hardly any use thinking we can raise this child comfortably. I must fully trust that only God will protect him. Often I pray during my daily work. I try to sing, but my mind is too fearful. I guess you don't understand."

"Well, Marie, you've gone through this so often, but you must drown out those awful thoughts. Look on the bright side. Thus far, God has always spared his life, even without any injuries.

"The gossiping and nasty remarks of Mark, the herdsman, didn't do much harm to the colony," Sara added. "Mark was fired and has left the village. Ever since this baby was born, he was always angry and unfriendly toward you folks and us—simply because we cared for him. How he might be involved is only our guess. But now we're rid of him."

As Isaac Harders opened the door to leave, it was snowing. The ground was white. John's dog wagged his tail in a fast motion as he sniffed the surroundings outside the Derksen house.

"What's up, Rosy? You're alarmed about something."

John and Ike trailed him and saw footprints outside the house and back through the garden. "They look like woman-sized feet," said Ike, "and it plainly shows that someone was outside, spying on us."

John decided not to tell Marie about it so she would sleep well. He could keep control of his nerves fairly well. That way, he was able to comfort her.

The winter turned out to be quite cold, yet without much snow. The Heuboden folks mostly stayed at home and inside, to stay warm.

Marie kept the kitchen warm the best she could to guard her precious baby from getting sick. She held him and often cuddled him by the stove. John did not go looking for work. They took time to enjoy their child.

The Derksen couple was so happy and often praised God and read the Holy Word. One evening they read Jesus' words from Matthew 7: "Do not cast your pearls before swine, lest they trample them under their feet, and turn again and rend you."

"I guess our boy surely was a pearl cast to the swine," mused John. "Is that what this means, Marie?"

"Could be, but I don't understand all the Scripture. At least we can treasure our own precious pearl." She gave Baby Johann an extra hug and a kiss as she tucked him into his cradle.

☙ 11 ❧

A Sad Death

At the far north of this Mennonite village was a tavern, which attracted some men to the habit of drinking. None could afford it, but the evil spirit in their hearts had taken a tight grip on some. Their parents and wives begged and cried that they would stay out of the bar. Some young women suffered tremendously for lack of food and saw their innocent children undernourished.

This evil problem bound twenty-eight-year-old Gerhard Penner. He spent many cold winter days at the tavern.

His wife, Anna, often tired and weary, worried about this dilemma. "What will become of our three innocent little children?" she wondered. She was not feeling well the past few weeks, and each day she begged her husband to stay home.

One day, out of regard for what other folks would think, he stayed home to care for her as she lay on the matted straw bed. In the late afternoon, little Peter was born in the cold house. Their heating supplies were scarce. The poor woman worried over how the infant would survive with old worn-out baby clothes that she had saved from three other births.

When the neighbors heard of the situation, they asked Mayor Peters for advice. Mrs. Peters was quite upset and had a few things to say.

"My, oh my, how foolish for him not to care more for the sweet and loving wife he married seven years ago," said Susanna. "His parents taught him well, but he became addicted by keeping company with lower-class men and boys. How I wish that the ministers could warn them enough never to start drinking. Every time it turns out to be a heartbroken marriage, with hate and hunger, untrue love, lying, and a guilty conscience.

"Someone told me that he's so deep in debt at the tavern that he's thinking of selling his only cow. Then the young ones won't have any milk to drink. They'll turn to skin and bones."

Susanna Peters visited a few homes, inquiring whether anyone had a few diapers and gowns for the newborn. She collected an armful. Anna Penner cried in appreciation for such goodness. "Our baby, Peter, might not need to freeze. Thank you, thank you for your kind heart and action."

Nevertheless, after giving birth, Anna Penner could not regain her strength. She lay in bed for three weeks. Gerhard stayed at home, caring for his wife and four children the best he could. He had kept the cow.

A few evenings later, when the children were tucked under the few covers in the chilly room, he again went for a drink. Anna grieved in her loneliness. While her husband was still away, a few men entered the house, planning to take away the chest where the family's clothes and blankets were kept. Since it was winter and everything was in use, the chest was empty.

"No, no," said Anna softly, "you may not take the chest. That is mine; my mother gave it to me."

"But your husband bargained to give it to us, to pay off his debt of liquor," they replied as they carried it toward the door.

"Please, you may take anything else," she cried bitterly, "but leave the chest here. I want it to stay in the family."

Her sobbing tears touched the two men's hard hearts, and they left the chest.

She was so heartbroken that her husband would make such a deal. After the men left, she moaned, "What will ever need to happen to change my husband's sinful habit?" The baby began to cry, but she could not get up. She was too exhausted.

Back at the bar, the two angry men approached Gerhard. "That chest belongs to your wife and not you. We pitied her too much to take it." Holding a powerful fist in Gerhard Penner's face, one of them shouted, "I want my money from you somehow, you no-good hoodlum. Understand?"

Gerhard was too drunk to pity his wife. "You didn't get the chest?" he growled. "Come on! I have authority over my house. I bargained to give it to you, and you shall have it. We can lay the clothes and blankets on the floor."

When he reached home with the other two men, he snapped at his sick wife: "That chest is sold. If I say it's sold, then it's sold.

I have no other choice. You didn't approve of me selling the cow. I need to shake off this debt. I promise that I will not buy any more drinks."

The poor, weak woman cried and cried. "Before our marriage, I never dreamed that I would ever have a husband who would sell most of my furniture to pay off his debts of beer and whiskey. Someday you might be awfully sorry for this, if God's wrath comes upon you."

As she fainted on the pillow, she prayed, "O God, have mercy on him."

At her husband's command, the men took the chest.

Gerhard tried to keep his commitment, but he could not. Satan was too powerful. Anna wanted him to pray with the family. He could only sound out a few words and stumbled in his praying. She prayed whenever she had enough strength, and yet she felt that God heard her tiny groans.

Anna Penner's life was ebbing away. She had no appetite and did not eat. One day three of her caring friends—Marie Derksen, Sara Harder, and Susanna Peters—sat at her bedside.

"I cannot endure this pain much longer," Anna said. "But I also wish that I could have someone to take care of my loving little baby. How is he doing?" she asked the mayor's wife.

Marie took hold of her hand. "Oh, you blessed mother! I know it is hard for you. I also have experienced much sorrow in my young life. Leave everything in God's hands. Someday he will ease your burdens. God was so kind to let you have four children. He let you see your little Peter before you die."

Marie kissed the sick woman, and her warm tears dripped upon the face of her dear friend.

The other two women cried, thinking her desire was to be with Jesus, where all her earthly troubles would be no more.

Anna asked the women to pray for her husband, and also to pray that she may be faithful till her end. She was so weak.

A few days later, Marie came to see how Anna was. She noticed that Anna was feeling better. Her eyes showed a bit of spark, and her speech was not so faint.

"Good morning, Anna. You look somewhat better, so bright! How great!"

"Yes, I feel free." She smiled. "Last night while Gerhard was snoring on the floor beside the stove, I heard a sweet voice: *You are going on a journey. Get ready to go soon.*"

Marie sensed what it meant. She sat at her bedside. "Blessed, blessed friend. How you have suffered. I think the angels are coming for you. May you rest in peace."

"Will you take care of my children? Promise me you will. If they have no mother, where will they stay after I am gone?"

"Yes, I promise you that somebody will take care of them. I will share my love as I can, the same as I do for our little Johann."

Now Anna knew that she could depend on what Marie said. Her work on earth was done. She longed to be in heaven.

Gerhard heard his wife's concerns. He felt unworthy of not caring enough for his children.

Marie saw that her end was near. She ran to ask Sara Harder to come.

"Now, what happened?" exclaimed Sara, seeing Marie's sad face. "Did something happen to little Johann?"

"No, no. Anna Penner is dying, I think. Please come. I don't want to stay alone with Gerhard."

Sara sent the children to ask Mrs. Peters to come along. A few other women came, too.

Gerhard sat at the table with a scowling face. He felt so sorry that he was not a better husband, but it was too late.

The four sorrowing women stood at the bedside in total silence. A faint smile was on Anna's face as she lay there, with her three-week-old baby in her arms. She had asked her husband to place it there.

Gerhard had gone outside, trying to free himself from the awful strain that swamped him.

Anna called for her husband, and so Susanna Peters asked him to come back in. As he stood by her bed, she said, "Give me your hand."

Her feeble thin hands clung to his hand as she said in a weak voice: "I will soon be leaving you. The angels are coming. I know I often did not do my duty as I should have. Can you forgive me? I can forgive all your mistakes and ask the good Lord to forgive you, too. Promise me that you will be a good father to our children. My death will be much easier if I can hear that promise."

At these words, her head slumped back into her pillow. Gerhard fell on his knees. In his distraught sorrow, he buried his face in the blanket and wept like a little child.

After a while, she struggled to sit up in bed, but she couldn't. She placed one hand on his head and murmured: "Soon I am gone. Come a bit closer. I want to look into your eyes one more time."

He got on his feet, bent over her, and kissed her for the last time. She placed her weak arm over his neck as his tears wetted the pale face. Soon her arm slowly slipped off, dropping upon the straw tick. Gerhard sat back on a chair.

Anna opened her eyes a bit. In a whisper, she said, "Water." Marie wetted her lips, but she didn't drink. The room was totally quiet except for the sounds of her gasping for breath.

"He's coming, he's coming," and she whispered a few more words too faint to detect. Finally her breathing stopped, and her head lay to the side. She was gone.

Her husband stood at her bed and cried for a while. He looked up at Marie and said, "I had a good wife, much more than I deserved."

The women notified the neighbors, and they came to share their sorrow with Gerhard.

Before long, Preacher Wiebe arrived with some songbooks. He quoted Jesus' words from John 8:51: "Verily, verily, I tell you, whoever keeps my word will never see death."

As they stood around Anna's deathbed, these believers sang a hymn of acceptance, affirming their faith, hope, and love:*

Grablied

Geht nun hin und grabt mein Grab,
Denn ich bin des Wanderns müde!
Von der Erde scheid' ich ab,
Denn mich ruft des Himmels Friede,
Denn mir ruft die süße Ruh
Von den Engeln droben zu.

* "Grablied" (1819), by Ernst Moritz Arndt (1769–1860), translated by Catherine Winkworth (1855).

Geht nun hin und grabt mein Grab!
Meinen Lauf hab' ich vollendet,
Lege nun den Wanderstab
Hin, wo alles Ird'sche endet,
Leget mich ins Grab hinein,
Wo ich ruhe von der Pein.

Ihr, die nun in Trauer geht,
Fahret wohl, ihr lieben Freunde!
Was von oben niederweht,
Tröstet ja des Herrn Gemeinde.
Weint nicht ob dem eitlen Schein,
Droben nur kann Ew'ges sein.

Weinet nicht, daß ich nun will
Dieser Welt den Abschied sagen,
Daß ich aus dem Irrtum will,
Aus den Schatten, aus den Plagen,
Aus dem Eitlen, aus dem Nichts
Hin ins Land des ewegen Licht's.

Weinet nicht! mein wahres Heil,
Meinen Heiland hab' ich funden;
Und auch ich hab' ja mein Teil
An den Heil'gen Todeswunden,
Woraus einst sein teures Blut
Floß der ganzen Welt zu gut.

Weint nicht, mein Erlöser lebt!
Hoch vom finstern Erdenstaube
Hell empor die Hoffnung schwebt,
Und der Himmelsheld, der Glaube,
Und die ewege Liebe spricht:
"Kind des Vaters, weine nicht!"

Funeral Song

Go and dig my grave today!
Weary of my wand'rings all,
Now from earth I pass away,
For the heav'nly peace doth call;
Angel voices from above
Call me to their rest and love.

Go and dig my grave today!
Homeward doth my journey tend,
And I lay my staff away
Here where all things earthly end,
And I lay my weary head
In the only painless bed.

So farewell, ye much-loved friends!
Grief hath smote you as a sword,
But the Comforter descends
Unto them that love the Lord.
Weep not o'er a passing show,
To th' eternal world I go.

Weep not that I take my leave
Of the world; that I exchange
Errors that too closely cleave,
Shadows, empty ghosts that range
Through this world of nought and night,
For a land of truth and light.

Weep not, dearest to my heart,
For I find my Savior near,
And I know that I have part
In the pains He suffered here,
When He shed His sacred blood
For the whole world's highest good.

Weep not, my Redeemer lives;
Heav'nward springing from the dust,
Clear-eyed Hope her comfort gives;
Faith, Heav'n's champion, bids us trust;
Love eternal whispers nigh,
"Child of God, fear not to die!"

As they closed the songbooks, they heard the little baby crying. He was hungry. Marie asked a few of the women who had babies if they would nurse little Peter. They consented and cared for him for a while.

Two days later most of the Heuboden folks attended the funeral. It was hard to dig the grave in the frozen ground. Many tears flowed as the men lowered Anna's body into the earth on this bitterly cold day in January.

Gerhard had promised to be a good father to his children. He stayed at home with the three preschoolers. During the winter months, his friends were at the tavern. They begged him to come again, but he did not yield to temptation. He was lonesome, and he knew well enough that he needed to lead a Christian life if he wanted another companion to help raise his children.

Since Gerhard had spent all his money on liquor, he was totally broke. The villagers brought food for the Penner family so they could survive. He proved to be a good father and kept the house fairly warm, burning what little straw and cowchips he had. Baby Peter received care at a friend's house.

☙ 12 ❧

The Second Wife

The birds were singing again as the Russian earth thawed out from the long cold winter. The roads were bad, and the soft mud clung to the wheels and feet of horses and humans. A tint of green leaves spread over the trees as the warm sunshine aroused new pleasure among the villagers. Again the herder was taking the cows to pasture on the outlying slopes.

As the folks gathered for Sunday services, they were rather surprised to see Gerhard Penner and the three children coming with the widower's girlfriend. The warm sunshine matched the love evident among the whole congregation. The secret was leaking out that the bishop would announce the wedding for Gerhard and his girlfriend that day. The meetinghouse was full. A minister from a far-off village had planned to be present.

Marie shed a few tears as she talked with the young woman. "Helena, this is just a real pleasure to see that you want to accept Gerhard and his four children. Little Peter is such a sweet darling. He needs a mother. I'm sure you will love him."

The Scripture text was about Joseph when his brothers left Egypt with their sacks of grain upon the donkeys' backs. One message the preacher brought forth was "Do not quarrel along the way."

After the service, the two were betrothed to be married in the church two weeks later.

The visiting minister went home with John and Marie Derksen. From far around, people knew John as a doctor of natural cures, using herbal tea and other remedies. They actually called him "Doctor Derksen," and through folk medicine he healed many people with various health problems. The preacher had an ailment and wanted John's help while he was in Heuboden.

After Marie served dinner, they visited, and Marie began talking about their little boy, Johann, explaining how he became their foster son. She imagined that folks far around had heard about the dreadful act of someone trying to dispose of a baby.

Later in the afternoon, the Derksens mentioned the life of Gerhard Penner and how Anna had been such a devoted wife.

"I hope he will be good to this new bride," said the minister, "although I know nothing about any of them."

Two weeks later Gerhard and Helena were married after the Sunday services. The preacher reminded them how nice married life can be if both do more than their share for each other. Now again, Gerhard had a wife, and the children a mother.

In late June, the blazing hot sun beat down upon the dry soil. The days were long, and the night hours did not bring much relief from the heat. Since the beds were too warm, many slept on the wooden floors or outdoors on the dry, parched lawns.

Their small plots of corn became wilted, the vegetable gardens stunted. The lush green pasture for hillside grazing turned brown. Milk became scarce for the hungry children.

"If we don't get rain soon, our wheat will not amount to much," said Ike Harder. "We won't have any flour to bake bread. We'll likely have to grind barley for flour. It doesn't make as good bread as wheat flour does. At Schönfeld they raise some turkeys. Maybe they will share some with us."

"We must pray harder for rain," said Sara. "It's all in God's hands. If we pray, perhaps we will have enough food to store for winter use."

Finally the rains came, but too late to save the wheat. So the villagers ground barley into flour. That gave them some work again in place of sitting under the shade trees to find relief from the heat. Since they had no thermometers, they could not record degrees for the temperature.

After the hot summer months, the winter of 1864 was harsh. Bitter cold weather with much snow kept the folks housebound for many days. Huge white snowdrifts blew around the crude buildings, which lacked insulation. A great responsibility hung over the Heuboden parents as they reckoned with the low supply of food stored up for humans and cattle to use in the winter.

Mrs. Neufeld occasionally worked at Erdman Buhren's place in exchange for some food to help feed her family of four school-age children. While going to work, this forty-year-old widow found it hard to walk through the snowdrifts. It was not fit for children to venture outside. This mother was determined to keep her family from starving.

One day Erdman gave her a loaf of rye bread for a Christmas gift, which they celebrated on January 6. On that Christmas morning, the children did not expect any presents. There were none—no money to spend.

After the children had eaten their *daily* limited supply of barley bread, their mother brought forth the loaf of rye bread. Now she allowed them to eat the whole loaf, which filled their stomachs once more.

As the cold weather continued, the animals suffered along with the humans. The desperately cold wind blew for days, turning the small barns into frigid, cruel stables. A few four-month-old calves froze, and also some pigs were frozen in the barns. After they thawed out again, the villagers cut off some pieces of meat for human consumption. Meat was scarce, and folks did not want to waste any edible food.

Every living creature welcomed the spring of 1865 as the warm rains brought forth green grass again. No human being froze to death, but plenty of them had frostbitten ears, fingers, and toes during the cold months.

Little Johann Derksen also survived the cold winter. He was growing, and Marie enjoyed playing with him, telling him stories, and so on. They had no children's storybooks or store-bought toys.

Johann had no reason to believe that this was not his real mother. Marie hoped that he would never find out how his young life was in great peril. She feared that in his school days the older children might mock him, telling him that the Derksens were not his real parents. Marie dared to think that his childhood days would pass without him hearing nasty remarks of being born in the hog pen.

During the day, her husband had again gone to work in another settlement, helping on a farm. At sunset quite a few of the village men met at the center of the village, leaning on the gates and discussing their daily work. They gathered news and shared conversation with their neighbors. The summer songbirds quieted down as the nightingale gave its song at dusk.

After a long walk home, John enjoyed the fellowship of other men. He was glad for work but missed being with his little one during the daytime hours.

The days fled by swiftly for Marie since she had a three-year-old to chat with. Often people could hear her singing as she went about her work. Life was pleasant. The women frequently visited together and shared their joys and sorrows. They talked about their gardens and children.

People reported seeing some teenage boys occasionally outside the tavern. The mothers' eyes smarted with sad tears. At night they prayed while rocking their youngest child to sleep. They prayed while at work in the house or in the garden.

Mothers prayed not only that God would keep their own children from getting involved in this sin, which could last for nearly a lifetime, but also for all the young folks. Parents knew that if their children's friends were involved in lustful sins, their own children were also tempted.

A few women visited at Gerhard Penner's house one day. They soon noticed that his new wife, Helena, was somewhat quick-tempered with the children.

Little one-and-a-half-year-old Peter came toddling into their circle with a ball of yarn, unrolling it as he went. His stepmother screamed at him: "Peter, you naughty rascal, how many times have I scolded and spanked you for messing with my sewing basket?"

Helena grabbed the scared child by the arm and gave him a hard spanking right in the midst of the other women. She took the crying toddler to his crib and slapped his mouth. "Now, shut up!"

As she entered the circle again, one of the women warned her: "You'd better be careful or you'll make a disrespectful boy out of him. Please treat him with love and kindness at such a young age. His own mother would be heartbroken if she were still living. Children will hardly ever turn out well if they are treated so harshly when young. Please be kinder to the little boy."

"Yes, I know," replied Helena. "But Peter tests my patience so terribly. While I was setting the table yesterday, he pulled off the tablecloth and broke two of my dishes, which were more precious than he is. He's always getting into mischief as soon as I turn my back."

"What does Gerhard say about such harsh treatment?" asked another woman. "Does he paddle him?"

"Huh," she snorted, "he is simply too unconcerned to raise these children. This house would look a fright if I wouldn't be around for one day. Furthermore, don't I have the right to make these youngsters behave? If they would be allowed to do whatever they get into their silly minds, then you ladies would say, 'The Penner children don't get taught anything.'"

Marie and the group of women were sad as they left the house. "It's too bad that God took these little children's mother away," said one. "I can see that she is still needed, though when she died, I was glad that she did not need to live longer since her husband was such a drunkard."

"I thought that Helena and I could share things together," Marie commented, "since we both have children who are not our own. But I can see that she is not giving or sharing much love with them. Surely the three oldest ones often cry for their real mother. Oh, I pity them so. I'm afraid she'll cripple one yet. I would be willing to take all four of them into my house, and my little Johann would be very happy to have children to play with."

As Marie walked across the yard, little Johann ran to meet her. She picked him up and held him tightly to her chest. "Oh, you little darling," she cried.

Right there Marie asked God never to let hate enter her heart over her only child's behavior.

☙ 13 ❧

Pushed into the Creek

That year the folks of Heuboden enjoyed a fine growing season. The wheat harvest was good, better than average. Things appeared to be more prosperous. The barns sheltered plenty of winter hay and corn. The women also stored plenty of dried food whenever and wherever they could. Some houses had no cellars.

At the tavern the waitress noticed better sales again as the winter approached. Was prosperity the answer? Yes, she had experienced this pattern before. The men could not buy drinks without money.

One evening a familiar-looking man appeared at the hotel, but only to play a game of cards with his old buddies. At the death of his first wife, Gerhard Penner had fully decided never again to drink any liquor. He had promised Anna that he would be a good father to their four children.

Gerhard meant what he promised. He was a good father for a while, but he was unhappy to see how Helena treated the children. He tried to remind and admonish her in a friendly manner.

But she slammed back: "If you would be in the house all day with these unruly stepbrats, you would lose your temper, too."

Helena did not accept her husband's way of telling her how to raise the children, whom she called "stepbrats." She claimed that she knew how. He decided to let her have her way rather than argue in the presence of his children.

"I'll go and enjoy myself at the tavern," he muttered to himself. Yet he nearly let himself be sidetracked. Playing cards at the tavern was not the only remedy Satan offered to relieve his troubled thoughts. His buddies offered him a shot of whiskey to comfort him for the loss of his first wife.

Gerhard explained his problems at home. "Well, if your new wife doesn't obey what you say about the kids, I'd let her ride," one said.

"Have your fun here with us," they urged. "Let her be boss. My wife also gets nasty at times."

Gerhard did not accept the free drink. On the way home he looked up to see how bright the moon was. Now his thoughts turned to Anna in heaven. "Oh, how nice it might be up there. It looks so peaceful." He felt like praying, and he did pray, but with only a few words.

As he entered the cozy kitchen, Helena asked in a gruff voice: "Where've you been? The children have been waiting to go to bed till you came in. They said you're not in the barn. I didn't have any reason to go and look for you."

He went with the boys to hear them say their prayers as their real mother always did, then said, "Good night, boys."

"Good night, Daddy," they responded. Now they felt more comfortable and were soon asleep.

"Were you out drinking?" Helena grilled him.

"No, I wasn't. I promised Anna I wouldn't touch that stuff again. I hope to hang on to that commitment."

Helena was not enthused about praying together. She wanted to do things her way, without the help of the Lord.

Weeks slipped by. The children were afraid of her, and Gerhard was at the hotel more often. At last he gave up his promise and began drinking again. He declared to himself that he would not have done so if he would have a loving wife.

"Is the Lord punishing me now?" Gerhard asked himself. "Do I lack a good marriage because I was not a faithful husband to my first wife?" Hoping things would go better, he often cried to himself: "This life is so hard, and I pity the children."

One evening Uncle Wiebe said to Isaac Harder, "Well, the way it looks, we need to look for another schoolteacher. Our teacher is moving to Burwalde. I met him yesterday and pleaded with him to stay, but he decided to go ahead as planned. He says it's best to change schools before problems get too bad. I wish they would ask Abram Enns. He's a good teacher."

The next October the village hired another teacher. He was rough and whipped the children for any reason or excuse he could find.

Doctor Derksen, Marie's husband, was busy in the wintertime. Now John could afford a horse and open buggy to make house calls instead of walking or riding horseback with his satchel. He drove to a few other villages, too.

From quite a few families he was hearing of the rough schoolteacher Knelsen, but some mothers did not say a word about the situation. Later he found out why: the teacher had given the children strict orders that anyone who tattled to the parents would get the most painful whipping they had ever had.

John told Marie of these poor children with bruised bodies. "A mother showed me a few of them today. They had black-and-blue streaks across their backs and rear ends. The parents kept them home today. The children are so fearful that they hardly talk to their parents about school."

The parents expected the teacher to guide their children in reading the *Fibel*, a German primer for beginners; the New Testament for middle-graders; and the Bible for the older students. If the parents heard no complaints, they figured that things were going smoothly at school. Occasionally some parents reminded the teacher to use the stick if the students would not obey. To the parents, Teacher Knelsen did not mention any problems.

"Oh my, John," sighed Marie. "I sure hope another teacher will be hired before our little son goes to school in a few years."

Johann's preschool years were happy. He enjoyed playing with Gerhard's son Abram. Johann's mother taught him love and respect, and she told him about Jesus and the good God in heaven.

But Abram heard little of this God. Johann shared and talked about the Bible with Abram, who believed the kind words. "My mother and dad pray every morning and evening," said Johann. "We fall on our knees and talk to God and Jesus. In the morning we ask God to protect us from any harm. In the evening Dad prays, reading from a little black book, thanking the good God for all the good things. Don't your parents pray?"

"My first mother often prayed, but my new mother doesn't think it's necessary. My mother Anna also used to sing, but this one doesn't. I wish we would still have our first mother. I don't know why she died," cried the sad boy, with tears streaking down his face.

The innocent little boys played and shared their joy and sorrow as they roamed the fields and hillsides. They had no idea what sadness they would see later in life.

One evening as five-year-old Johann was coming back home after running an errand for his father, he walked beside a little stream. The fall evening was cool, and yet he wore no coat. He enjoyed tossing little stones into the water and watching the ripples.

He did not realize that anyone else was near. Then suddenly some woman behind him screamed and pushed him into the water. After emerging in his wet clothes, he saw a stern-faced woman standing on the bank.

A year earlier Johann's mother had told him that there was a bad woman around, in one of the villages. "Stay away if you see anyone like that. She might harm you." Now Johann remembered that warning.

The scared and dripping-wet boy cried in anguish as he ran up the opposite bank into the bushes a distance away. He lay down between the hedges, cold and frightened. As he peered out, he saw her standing on the other bank, waiting for him. Evidently she did not want to get wet while crossing the creek. At twilight she finally left. John shivered terribly as he decided: "This is that mean woman my mother told me about."

Johann did not know that she was his birth mother. She was still watching for a chance to destroy his life when no one would see her. She apparently had tried to drown him.

So even after five years, her guilty conscience still plagued her for the sin she had committed as a teenager. Surely that sin was not worthwhile. She could not stand to see her offspring enjoy the beauty of life while anger still imprisoned her own life. An evil spirit still held a tremendous grip on this unmarried woman, who suffered many nights without sleep.

Johann hardly dared to stand up. "What did I do wrong that she pushed me into the stream?" he wondered.

He lay there for a few hours, becoming awfully cold. At last he decided to head for home, praying as he walked in the dark but starry night. Johann tried to go quietly, wading back across the unfamiliar stream. His mother had warned him not to wade in the water, fearing that he might slip and drown, but he had to get home somehow.

Marie had told Johann that she often prayed for him, that no harm would befall him. He thought, "Surely Mother and Dad are both praying for me now, since I'm out at night." Several times he stopped to listen, to detect whether that lady might be sneaking up on him.

Now he heard his mother's voice from a distance: "Johann—Johannnn—Johnny, where are you?" Marie occasionally liked to call him Johnny.

Soon he was clasped in his mother's strong arms. They both cried as she stroked her soft hand over his cold head. "My, oh my, Johnny, where were you? Why didn't you come home before dark? Your clothes are wet."

She carried her sobbing darling into the kitchen, and he told her what had happened.

"Oh, Johann, I had no idea you were out in the darkness alone. I thought you might be at Penners' place."

After Marie dressed him in dry clothes, she warmed up the leftovers from supper. "After this, you must stay closer to home."

"I don't like to play inside the Penners' house," explained the frightened Johann. "Abram's mother is very unkind to the children. He showed me his bruises the other day."

ଔ 14 ଓ

Hard School Days

On a frosty morning in October 1869, Johann started off to school, making the two-mile walk to Schönfeld. He looked forward to this the same as every young child does. The villagers had hired another teacher, from the Schönfeld area. The parents hoped that he was a good-natured and civilized man.

The first day of school, Johann wasn't quite sure if school was going to be what he had hoped for. The second day teacher Regehr showed the children the long hickory twig he had brought along. He was a man of few words and mentioned no rules. He figured that the pupils knew how a schoolroom was supposed to be run.

A few weeks later, two girls, Helena Dyck and Gretchen Wiebe, were busy studying their books in their double-seat desk when the teacher thought they were whispering with each other.

He came up in back of them and lashed them two hard blows with the hickory switch. Both yelled in surprise and fear, crying at the intense pain. The teacher growled, "Study, and no whispering."

It was no use for them to explain that they were not whispering. He ruled the classroom with anger and hate. No love abounded anywhere. The children trembled in fear. Their tense nerves retarded their study. They could not think properly.

These two girls were the oldest of the twenty-three pupils. The teacher did not like them because they had a better education than he had. He watched for their mistakes so he could have an excuse to punish them. Also, he harshly warned them not to speak of school to their parents: "This is my school. Understand?"

One day he punished these two girls for a minor error. A few posts inside the schoolroom helped to support the roof when heavy snow fell. The teacher ordered the two girls to stand at the front of the room where everyone could see them, back to back with a post between them. He took off their felt caps, tied under their chins with long strings, and used the strings to tie their heads tightly against the post. Their faces ached with intense pain as tears squeezed out of their eyes.

"Now tell each other what needs to be said in school hours," he yelled. He turned to the other pupils and shouted, "No more whispering!" as he slammed his hand down on his desk.

Gretchen was still living when this book was first printed in 1944. Johann Derksen, Abram Penner, and Abram Dyck were good chums at this school. A son and daughter of this Abram Dyck were also living in 1944. They remember their father talking of these rough school days.

Marie Derksen worried about others possibly mocking Johann for being a foundling or being adopted. She felt sure that the strict ruling of the teacher would not allow any such thing. But she was entirely wrong.

Abram Penner's stepmother treated Abram harshly. Now in school, it was worse yet. The Dyck family was among the poorest folks in Heuboden. Instead of pitying this family, the teacher ridiculed them for wearing shabby clothes.

One day three of the little boys were so stressed with fear that they could not recite what the teacher taught them. He set them on what was called the lazy bench.

This was new to these little boys. They did not know what would happen. One of them, Johann, walked over to an older girl, asking what he did wrong.

"Stay sitting on the lazy bench, hog rascal," scolded the teacher as he grabbed him by one ear. "What's your problem?"

"Ow, ouch!" screamed Johann, suffering terrific pain. He cried and cried and wished to run home.

At noon recess the children played ball. For Johann, this appeared to be fun. As the ball rolled way out, Johann decided to run after it. He wanted to help play.

When he brought the ball back, a big boy gave him a hard kick on his leg. "Let your hands off that ball, you little hog rascal. This is our game."

Johann ran to Gretchen, who hugged and comforted him. "Don't cry, Johann, or the big boys will laugh at you."

He decided that the big boys were as rude as their teacher.

Gretchen told him, "I think that if the pupils would be taught love and kindness, they would all play nicely together. I sure hoped that we would have a nice teacher this term. Come, I'll play with you. I love you. You and I will be buddies, okay?"

Johann tried to stay away from the big boys' territory. Right then he made up his mind that when he became a big boy, he would never mistreat little pupils as the big boys had done to him.

So Johann's first two months of school turned out to be sorrow instead of joy. He learned much, but most of it was about evil and rudeness.

"Now you three lazy lubber boys, come up here to my desk," said the teacher. "It's time you get something worthwhile in your heads.

"What kind of book do you have in your hand, Johann?"

"A *Fibel* [primer]."

"Good," answered the teacher.

Johann could hardly believe his ears to hear a good comment from him.

"And what picture is on the front page?"

"A horse."

"Right. And what is on the next page, Abram?"

"A dog."

"Very good. And what does the dog do, Abram Dyck?"

The three beginners did not know exactly what the proper answer might be. They knew that dogs do many different things. As they looked at the teacher questioning, someone from the classroom answered, "He bites."

The teacher could not detect the source of the voice, and everyone was deeply engrossed in their lessons. This burned up the teacher.

"What else does the dog do, Johann?"

"He barks."

The next page showed the partridge, and Johann named it before the teacher asked.

"Wasn't your turn, smart piggy," scoffed the teacher.

"Tomorrow we'll see a pig in the book. Then you may say it. Ha-ha."

Johann was totally innocent about the pig talk. He figured it was just farm language.

When he reached home, Marie sat beside him on the bench and asked, "Well, Johnny, how did you enjoy school today?"

"A big boy kicked me, but I knew my lessons. But what does the teacher mean by calling me a lazy hog rasc?" He couldn't even say the strange word "rascal."

Marie quivered as she thought: "Oh no, the poor boy! And the teacher will tell the children, no doubt. Why must he be ridiculed for the sin of his real mother, who gave him birth?"

She headed for the stable, where Johann would not see her, and cried: "Please, God, help him to enjoy school."

The next morning Johann was eager to go to school again. God had given him fresh courage through the other neighbor children. He was curious about what he might learn that day. His mother had wrapped a thick scarf around his neck, and they chatted together a while, waiting for other pupils to come along.

"Bye, Johnny."

"Bye-bye, Mother."

When Johann arrived at school, he stayed away from the big boys. They were playing ball again, but Johann only stood by the side of the schoolhouse.

He so enjoyed playing with other children because he had no brothers or sisters. And now he wasn't allowed to help play. He fought back his tears. "School is not what I thought it would be," he sniffed.

The teacher told the three little boys to study their books. Abram Dyck and Johann studied the wrong page because their little minds were so perturbed. They could not think properly for fear of the harsh teacher. When the teacher noticed that they had the wrong page, he yelled, "Wrong! The picture and word is 'house.' Why don't you scalawags pay attention."

He screamed "HOUSE" as he hit Johann over the head with a book so hard that he fell to the floor.

Abram knelt beside him and coaxed him to stand up again. He rubbed Johann's sore head as he whispered something in his ear: "All we can do is pray to Jesus. Somehow he will help us."

This kind action immensely irritated the teacher. He did not like to see anyone receiving pity. With each hand he grabbed a boy and marched them up to the front post. There he bound them back to back, on either side of the post, with heavy strings across their faces.

Johann slumped unconscious and hung there by the head. Abram screamed fiercely. Most of the other pupils were crying out of pity for the two little seven-year-olds.

One of the bigger girls, Agatha, took action. When the teacher had his back turned, she went up and rubbed her hand over both heads, but Johann was still in a daze. She was afraid he might die.

Before too long the teacher loosened the cords again, and the two boys staggered to their bench.

"Now, you all know that what goes on in school stays here. No tattling or complaining to your parents. Understand?" ordered the teacher as his hawk-like eyes scanned the classroom.

When the teacher dismissed school that day, all the pupils left the classroom in fear. Two big girls took the little boys by their hands. As the children walked away, the teacher watched them from the window.

At the supper table, the teacher told his wife, "I get so disgusted at those little ones. They simply know nothing!"

"Well, if you don't take care, you'll lose your job the same as Knelsen did," counseled his wife. "You must have more patience. How much did you know the first month when you were in school? You might have to suffer for this sometime. They are innocent children."

The two boys' mothers noticed their sons' bruises about their faces. "What are these marks?" asked Mabel Dyck.

Abram began to cry. He knew he was not allowed to tell. But his self-pity drove him to explain what had happened.

His mother was very upset at such harsh treatment. "Has this happened with any of the other children?"

He was crying and could hardly talk. "Yes, Johann was also tied tightly to the big post. One day two big girls were, also."

Abram's mother had pity on him whenever someone else

mistreated him. She went to talk with Sara Harder about it.

"Oh, this is horrible!" Sara exclaimed. "Our little Jacob came home the other day with his back hurt so badly that he couldn't walk straight. But he hardly told me why. I sensed that he was ordered not to tell us, and neither did our other children."

After a while, both women went to see how Johann Derksen looked.

"Come in," invited Marie. Sara and Mabel noticed Johann lying on a blanket by the brick oven.

"Oh, for pity's sake," moaned Marie. "These poor innocent little angels are being battered and bruised at school. My Johann's back was bleeding. I washed it off with warm water and rubbed healing salve on it. See the bruise marks on his cheeks and ears? He does not want to go to school again."

"One of our daughters said he lost consciousness when the teacher tied him to the post," reported Sara Harder. The three women simply cried.

"We don't need to put up with this," declared Sara. "I'm going to have Isaac go and tell Mayor Peters about this cruelty."

After supper Marie walked to Gerhard Penners. Gerhard wasn't home, so she started taking about the school situation with his wife, Helena. "Did little Abram tell you what happened in school today? I heard that he also got whipped."

"Yeah, he told me, but you know these youngsters need to be punished. It won't hurt them. I thought the parents wanted discipline in school."

"We do, but they can also be disciplined with love, not by crippling them. With such treatment, they'll become so mean mannered that they will never learn to love each other or their parents. I attended school, too, and I never experienced anything nearly like this."

"Oh, you're a lovely mother, aren't you?" Helena mocked. "If you had three rowdy boys in your care plus your husband going to the tavern, you'd be glad to have someone punish them."

Marie's feelings were hurt. As she hurried over to the mayor's place before dark, she sensed that he already would know about the school situation. "Are you coming about the little schoolboys?" Mayor Peters asked.

"Yes." Marie was glad to share her grief and cried as she also related the sad case.

In deep thought, the mayor bit his upper lips. His eyes blazed with power. He promised Marie that this would not occur again.

Mayor Peters went to his deacon for advice. They both went to the teacher's house. He saw them coming down the street.

With a stern look he greeted them: "Hi. What's up, you guys? Anything new? I noticed a few women fussing and talking as if there was a house fire somewhere, but I saw no smoke."

"Yes, we heard news, bad news," rejoined Peters, looking him straight in the eyes. "We came to question you about your cruel performance as schoolteacher.

"What's the reason for all this? You must simply hate your pupils. It is almost too horrible to think that a grown-up could have such hate in his heart to abuse them as we have heard. Why did you order them not to tell their parents? Don't you feel guilty? Were you treated this way when you went to school?

"These children did not tattle, but their mothers and fathers could see the bruises on their faces, and one boy could hardly walk when he came home. I'm asking you to quit this. You'll be sorry someday. God could smite you so that you suffer lots more than these innocent children."

"Huh, too bad. I'm the teacher, and I'll make my own rules. John Derksens have only this one child, and they are babying him like a lamb. Tell them to teach that hog rascal at home. He's an outcast. Who knows where he came from?"

This was too much for Mayor Peters. "Look, Mr. Regehr," he declared as he slammed his fist on the kitchen table, "this little Johann is a human being the same as you and I, created in God's image. How can you have such a hard heart as to class him as an animal?"

"And this little Abram Penner," added Deacon Wiebe, "how could you be so cruel to him? His stepmother does not show any love for him. It's awful that he is treated unkindly all day long."

"Well," countered the teacher, "Abram's mom says she is all for it, that these rowdy kids are taught discipline at school. They work on her nerves, and she needs rest."

"Mr. Regehr," rebuked Peters, "you know well enough that

we did not hire you to whip and cripple these children. Are you receiving what the parents agreed upon for your wages?"

"Yeah, from most of 'em," snapped Regehr. "Some bring one egg per child per week. Most of 'em give me a fourth pound of butter per child. Sometimes I settle for a bit of cream or a few potatoes. I'm not fussy. Some of the poorer families don't give me anything. You guys don't hear me complaining, do you? So then, why are you complaining? I don't intend to be a slave at that school."

"Well, okay, then. Try to be more gentle, especially to the younger ones," said Mayor Peters as they left. "Good-bye."

Mr. Regehr yelled after them: "You Heuboden folks aren't telling me how to run this school." He slammed the door shut with a crash.

"Peters' wife is putting him up to all this pitty-patty love stuff," he told himself. "She has no right to rule her husband. A mayor should stand on his own feet and make decisions on his own." He was mad and decided to enforce his rules as before.

As a result, the mayor and his assistant told the parents to keep the little ones at home.

A week later Jacob Buckert let a book fall off the bench. The teacher heard the sound and decided to try a different punishment if the parents did not allow him to whip pupils or tie them fast. He took a splinter of wood and carved the ends sharp with his pocketknife. The children's eyes peeped up at the teacher's desk, wondering what he intended to do.

"Come up here, Jacob. Open your mouth wide." Then the teacher stuck the pointed splinter behind the upper and lower lips, propping his mouth open. This caused terrible pain. Then Teacher Regehr told him to use one hand and hold the Bible up above his head as far as his arm could stretch. His arm became so tired that it slumped down before the hour of punishment was over.

Tears of pain dripped from the big boy's cheeks. He decided that he would run away if his dad made him attend this school another day. "I could never even treat a dog like this," he muttered to himself.

The whole classroom quivered with fear as they heard Jacob's painful groans.

This was too much for the village folks. Already that evening, Teacher Regehr lost his job.

Here I wish to present a question for all the schoolchildren in America: Do you appreciate your Christian teacher? If you don't, I advise you to change your mind. Be thankful that you can enjoy school life without fear such as these children had.

I also realize that without discipline in school, pupils would not learn true respect. Yet love never fails to abide in the classroom if teacher, parents, directors, and principal all use good common sense.

☙ 15 ❧

The Teacher Punished

Two days later the folks saw Teacher Regehr walking out of the village, without giving a good-bye to anyone. He was upset and did not want to accept the fact that he was fired. His wife wanted to stay, so he left without her, heading for a neighbor village nine miles away.

Mr. Regehr did not want the Heuboden folks to know where he was staying. A week later, his wife moved in with him. He was no longer a teacher and did not easily accept defeat, but he was unaware of his future.

His wife found a meager paying job because her husband claimed that he didn't feel well. He had no appetite and was miserable. She decided that he was just moody.

Finally he became so weak that he could hardly walk and was confined to bed. He had a problem in his stomach. They tried various kinds of herbal tea, but none brought relief. He could not rest. He groaned and screamed with pain.

At night the neighbors heard his loud cries. They wanted to comfort him by coming to visit, but he did not wish to see anyone.

At intervals while trying to sleep, with closed eyes he still saw scenes of his schoolchildren enduring severe pain and misery, being whipped or tied to the big post. In his dreams he saw their fears and tears.

Regehr screamed to God for pity, but his conscience told him that he did not deserve help from the Lord. He wished that he could see the face of Jesus instead of crying little boys. Often he bit his lips and clenched both fists, trying to quench the constant pain. "Oh, I am so miserable!" he yelled. "My stomach hurts."

His wife asked, "Should I ask Doctor Derksen to come? Surely he would know how to help you."

After three weeks of such misery, he finally consented to have the doctor come. It was a bit hard on his pride to have the dad of this little boy, whom he abused so rudely in school, come to help him in his own sufferings.

Regehr grumbled: "He will probably say, 'Didn't we tell you that God might smite you someday for being so cruel and harsh to these youngsters?' I don't want to hear that."

One night Doctor Derksen came at eleven o'clock, since he had been busy all day. Regehr had fallen asleep by the time the doctor arrived at his bedside. Derksen just stood there for quite a while, looking at the once-strong schoolteacher who had bruised and abused the innocent young children, now lying helpless on his stringy hard cot.

Suddenly the sick man's wild-looking eyes opened, and he began to rage and wave with both hands. He thought he saw the scholars again and said, "Come here, you little ones. I will not punish you any more. Give me water."

But the children did not come, and Regehr began howling and tossing his arms in misery. By now he could not walk or even sit up in his bed. He was so weak, and the pangs of hell tormented his mind.

Doctor Derksen thought of his own son, Johann. He asked the teacher if he should bring him here so that Regehr could apologize to him and the other children.

Yet from the evil teacher's actions and cussing language, Derksen saw that such a method would bring no good outcome. Even though the doctor gave Regehr a bit of good advice and showed him God's love, he could not help the tormented man.

"Good-bye, Mr. Regehr."

The ailing man made no response. The doctor left the house with deep thoughts on "how a person may appear at the judgment day before Jesus Christ and be cast into the torture of hell, which is uncountable times worse than what I have seen with Regehr. Yet the mayor had reminded him that this might happen if he kept on abusing his pupils."

The villagers hired Franz Dyck as teacher. He also was strict, but not like Regehr. His big brown eyes were sharp, and he left no mischief go unpunished, but he did not abuse the children. His own son attended this school.

Johann Derksen attended school again, but he did not learn

much. His first year of schooling was so hard because the others mocked him so often. He became self-conscious, desperately trying to do anything right.

Rather often he walked alone on his way home and hid behind the hill or among trees while the other children chatted on their homeward trek. He was afraid the evil woman would meet him again.

While hiding, he sometimes heard a fox's wild cry, which scared him. He shivered and crept close to the ground. Johann prayed to Jesus to calm his young mind as his parents had taught him to do if any trouble occurred when he was walking alone. He knew his mother was also praying, since she had told him that she did. She and her son could not forget the bad woman.

One evening as Marie sat in her kitchen, crying and waiting for Johann to come home from school, Aunt Sara Harder came to visit. "Well, are you crying about Johann again?" she asked. "Isn't he home from school yet? Our children have been home two hours already.

"I simply can't stand it that he needs to fear that woman, and that the other children don't care more about him. I've told ours to make sure he is safe even though the other children don't seem to care, but it's peer pressure, you know."

"Yes, I know," said Marie, "but I don't want to blame anyone's children. It sure is not easy to see our only child being treated so unkindly. Sometimes I wish he could just die and be with the schoolchildren in heaven.

"Abram Penner told him the other day that the bad woman is in the village again, so I don't expect him home till dark. Oh, when will this come to an end?" She sobbed loudly.

Dear readers: Surely as you read about the harsh school days of this young boy, you will no doubt wonder why the village folks did not find some way to protect him or have someone watch over him. They could well imagine that this evil woman might snatch him and take him out of the settlement.

Yet God no doubt was keeping him safe without human guards. Perhaps God sent an angel to protect this despised

little one, as Jesus suggests in Matthew 18:10 (also see Genesis 48:16).

God will not allow a praying mother's son to be harmed before that son has fulfilled his mission here on earth.

The children picked up rude behavior from harsh teachers. Too many of the richer folks' children mocked the youngsters of the poor folks.

The parents did not all feel the same about this foundling child Johann. Some thought he created more problems than they ever had in the village before.

These poor Mennonites sometimes received rough treatment from the rich. They wished to move away, to another settlement, but they could not afford to try it even if they found a new home.

Mayor Peters and the minister tried hard to solve this problem of two classes, poor and rich. Slowly the villagers again began to show more love among themselves. And yet no one had yet solved the mystery: they could not identify the mother of the innocent boy.

By hearing conversations about the bad woman and the adopted boy, little Johann sensed that he might be that boy. His parents still did not want to tell him, at his young age, about how he was rejected at birth. He had enough hardships to conquer, and he was becoming somewhat nervous with all the stress in his life.

ଓ 16 ଛ

From Mother to Mother

Johann's mother had a soft heart and let her true conscience be her guide, as her own dear mother had often reminded her before she died. Marie could hardly bear all this weight and worry any more.

"Why does our boy's life need to affect so many folks?" Marie asked her husband one evening as they waited for their son to come home. "All the gossip and rumors are wearing me out.

"Surely it is not God's will that he needs to be so scared, sleeping outside in his hiding place. I simply can't take it any longer." She cried into her handkerchief.

As dawn approached the next morning, Johann entered the kitchen. Marie served him a warm breakfast, but he could hardly eat as he watched his weary heartbroken mother.

After eating only half of his meal, he went to his dear mother, put his arms around her shoulders, and said, "Mother, dear, do not cry so much about me. I was not alone last night. Jesus was watching over me, and I slept well."

"Oh my, good for you. I hardly slept all night, worrying about you. I was praying most of the night that God would protect you. I know I should rely more on God.

"Little Johann, what will become of you if I might leave this world to go to a better home in heaven? I do not want to trouble you, but I am not feeling well the last two weeks."

Marie wrapped her arms around him and hugged her son firmly with the little strength she still had. Both cried and wept together till all their warm tears were shed.

Marie tried to explain to her seven-year-old son how she felt. "You know that your dad is a doctor, and he has done practically all he knows to make me feel better. But I am only getting weaker. Didn't you realize that I am very tired and walk slowly? I have a sickness that is hard to cure, your dad tells me."

"Yes, Mother, I noticed that you walk slow, but you did not cough and sneeze. I did not know that you are sick since you keep on working and making meals. When I am sick, I must lie in bed. Why don't you lie in bed?

"I will do the housework for you. I see that Dad is sometimes making breakfast the past while. Please, Mother, do get well soon. I can't live without you." He stroked her head softly.

A few days later Marie was confined to her bed. Her strength was fading, and her life slowly ebbed away. Little Johann and his dad cared for her, but she had no appetite.

After lying in bed for four weeks, one morning she called her son to stay and sit beside her, on her bed. She clasped her thin hand in his. "My poor boy, I feel awfully sorry for you. Will you promise to be a good boy when I die?"

Johann's eyes filled with tears. "Well, yes, Mother. Why do you ask? Am I not a good boy?" His tears dripped down on her cold hand.

In confusion, he crouched down close to her face. The boy was puzzled that his mother would ask this question.

Marie cried because of this love between mother and son. "Johann, I don't think I will get well again. I know you want to be a good boy."

Johann buried his sad face in her pillow and cried pitifully, "No, no, Mother. You dare not die and leave me. Oh, please, Mother, tell me that you will get well again. What can I do for you? I love you so much. Please, Jesus, help Mother get well again."

When he was cried out, she said, "Little Johann, you *are* a good boy. I know you do not understand, but Jesus knows I have had a hard life, and he knows I need a good sweet rest. As I often told you, good people may go to heaven when they die.

"If you will always be a good boy, you may go to heaven, too, someday. Then we may be together again. Father will be with you, and he will also pray for you that no one will hurt you. Remember, you also must pray often."

Father John saw and heard their crying as he stood at the foot of the bed. He was glad to hear his wife's earnest pleading. He also wept. It was so very hard for him that he could help other sick people but could find nothing to heal his own wife's illness. She had some pain, but mostly she was very miserable.

Sara Harder often came to help with the household duties and caring for Marie. She realized that Marie would hardly get well again. They discussed many things of the past and also of the future.

Once Marie held her hand and said, "I will soon be leaving this world. I saw angels flying above our house, and they were singing. An angel came by my bed and took my hand, saying, *We will soon come again and take you along*." Then Marie's hand fell limp.

Sara asked a neighbor for help. The two women stayed at the Derksens' place, taking turns in caring for Marie. She often asked for water but took only a few sips.

Before dark one evening, Johann went outside for a walk. On the street he met his best friend, Abram Penner. Johann explained what his mother had told him about dying.

Abram said, "Yes, my mother is also with the angels. She also said that if I am a good boy, I may be with the angels in heaven someday. Johann, you may also, but that bad woman may not.

"You and I will be good friends forever. If the other children or anyone else calls you a hog boy, they are liable not to get to heaven. My dear mother Anna told me that I shall never call you a hog boy because you are a boy just like all the other children."

During that night, Marie's breathing became harder. She often asked for a drink. The next morning a few kind neighbors came to see how Marie was. They prepared meals for that day.

When she awoke in mid morning, Johann went to her bedside again. He took her weak hand and said, "Mother."

She opened her eyes and whispered in a feeble voice, "Johann, my darling. Be obedient and trust in Jesus. Then you will be able to cope with your grief. Come, I want to kiss you one more time."

He bowed down unto her weary wrinkled face. His tears dripped again onto her cheeks. "Oh, Johann, you might cry many tears yet through life, but there is no harm in tears. Actually, they are a comfort and healing of sorrow."

After this, Marie could rest again. In the evening she began crying from some pain. She was very miserable. "Oh, it hurts so bad."

A few women besides Johann and his father sat around her bed all night. Marie lay there with a nice smile on her face as she slept. A few time her weak arms went up as if she was reaching for something.

As daylight approached, she asked for water again. "Now I see the angels coming. They are almost here and will take me along. Come, I am ready to go," she said as she lifted her hands again. Quickly they dropped as she breathed slower and then quit. Marie was dead.

Little Johann called her once more: "Mother, Mother!" But she did not answer. He lowered his confused head on her bed and wept. The poor boy was not as prepared for the death of his beloved mother as he thought he was.

When Marie's body was lowered into the grave, Johann finally wished her sweet rest. He was now without a mother. His father shared love with him and often talked of Marie to help in quenching their sorrow.

One day Abram Penner invited him to come and play with him in the yard. The two were happy, giving each other rides on the crude small wagon.

Suddenly Abram's stepmother yelled at them terribly. Both boys feared and quivered on the spot. She struck her son Abram some awfully hard blows over his back with the paddle stick.

Abram had no reason to think that he had done anything wrong. He lamented and cried as he fell over and stayed lying there. The pain was so severe that he could not get up. He wished his stepmother would die.

"And you," she screamed at Johann, "you no-good hog rascal, you'd better get going home before I whack your ears off. You have plenty of work since your mother is gone. I don't want you around here wearing down my nerves like you did to your mother. If she'd only let you lie in the hog pen, she could have had a good life."

The scared and shaky boy ran home as fast as his legs could take him. Although most of the Heuboden folks cared for Johann and treated him well, his young life was still quite hard.

For three days Abram did not come to school. On the fourth day, as Johann approached the Penners' house, Abram began walking toward school with Johann. The stepmother hollered out the door, "Don't walk with my son, you rascal."

At school Abram showed Johann his bruise marks on his back. Streaks of black-and-blue marks showed all over it. The poor boy could not walk straight.

Days and weeks passed. Little Johann was often alone in the house. Since his dad was a doctor, he was busy helping the sick. Time passed slowly for Johann. Fearing that the bad woman might come and get him, he hardly had enough courage to go out of the house when school was over.

He faithfully prayed every day, kneeling beside the empty bed where his loving mother had died. He remembered how she had told him that if he would pray, God would take care of him. For several years the evil woman didn't cause him any more problems. He truly believed that God heard his little prayers.

Ten months after Marie's death, the Heuboden folks were saying, "Doctor Derksen has found a woman friend, Tina." They stood in their yards as the two passed by in the buggy.

A week later they were married in the meetinghouse on Sunday morning. It was a big wedding because John Derksen was a prominent and good doctor and had many friends.

Now Johann had a new mother, and Tina was a good mother. He was happy again. Johann could feel her love as he sat beside her at the wedding. He sensed her protection for him.

☙ 17 ❧

Talking about America

One evening six months after his new marriage, John came home with news from the settlement about planning a migration to North America.

"That is far, far away. Who wants to migrate?" asked his wife, Tina. "Why do they want to move away from here?"

"I don't know. I think things are going better in our settlement," John replied as he sat down to eat supper.

Johann was confused about the subject but somewhat excited. His young mind soon told him that in America he might be rid of some of his former hardships.

"When will we go?" he asked. "Will we go with our horse and buggy?"

"No, no. We'll leave them here. We go with a train and a ship."

This was something new for the little boy to hear such words. He couldn't understand what was going on.

After the meal was finished, John said, "I'm going to talk with Mayor Peters to learn what really is the reason for this migration. It sounds rather foolish when things are going better in Heuboden and in the other settlements. Perhaps it is just a rumor."

The mayor was not at home. His wife said, "Yes, it is true, and quite a few folks are excited about leaving, but I am not convinced."

Late in the evening Mayor Peters arrived home. He explained to his wife and to John that the minister had received a letter from the government, ordering them to go to Odessa.

"Czar Alexander is requesting a money offering from the settlements, and he is stern with this demand."

"What do you think this means?" asked John.

"I'm not sure. Our neighboring Lutheran settlement also received a notice, and the czar explained what they have requested. It doesn't look good for us Mennonites. As I see it, our neighborly love is growing cold.

"Well, you know what happened a long while ago, and you possibly remember quite well what happened when the Molotschna Settlement released their shepherds. The authorities said the landowners must lease land to the landless."

"Yeah, I remember," said John. "But that was only the authorities' command."

"No, no. That was the law of the government. Yet instead of leasing the fertile ground to the poor peasants, the Mennonite landowners leased it to the rich so that they would have more money to buy land for the poor Mennonites."

"Well, that wouldn't be so bad," said John, "if they would have done that."

"They would have done that," said Mayor Peters, "but the landless weren't satisfied because they sensed that the government and the church would make a profit from the poor folks."

"Well, who will go to Odessa?" asked John.

"I don't know. On Friday is a meeting for some brothers at Schönfeld, and then we will find out."

John came home and told Tina what Mayor Peters said. She felt sad. "Will this be a huge migration? Will some of my family stay here?" She hesitated to think of the many folks who would leave their warm homes and leave personal belongings and livestock behind.

"But," said Tina, "we want to be true and steadfast to what our forebears and parents have taught us. We—more than our government authorities—must decide what God's plan is for us. We need God's blessing."

On Friday Minister Wiebe, Mayor Peters, and a good spokesman named Hiebert attended the meeting at Schönfeld. There it was decided that these three men and a few from the other settlements should start for Odessa on Monday, to meet with some officials. By the end of the week, they were back. They called a meeting for the settlements to explain what was in the future for the Mennonites in Russia.

Minister Wiebe said, "Yes, well, brothers, we were asked to sit in with the conference at Odessa. We were quite surprised at what we heard. The officials have decided to send our young men to Moscow, to teach them to honor the czar and participate in exhibitions at their shows and fairgrounds.

"We simply sat there speechless, wondering what kind of worldly spirit would be drilled into our youth. We knew that this would lead to military training for them. Finally I asked them, 'What is the benefit of this to you officials?'

"Their answer was, 'We are going to be your representatives and lead you folks.'

"I told them that we have a leader, Jesus, the King of all kings, who led our ancestors in their trials and hardships.

"Then they dismissed us, and we felt a heavy weight upon our shoulders. It looks very dark, the road ahead of us. What will our churches say? What mother or father would want their young boys to leave for Moscow? What shall we decide? The authorities are set on this decision.

"Wouldn't we rather think of a new home with religious freedom? I know this is a hard question that needs some utmost thinking.

"They asked us to come back after we have decided on an answer. As we stood in front of the general, Mayor Peters asked: 'If we would forward some money to help wounded soldiers and widows and orphans, would our young men be exempt from going to Moscow?'

"He said, 'The czar would thank you for the money,' but he made no other promise. We went back to our rooms very discouraged. There we had prayer and sang a few farewell songs together before we parted. We solely depended on God to show where he will lead us."

After all this, the talk among the villagers was America, the land of hope. Many appeared to be interested, but the old folks thought of their meager energy to endure such a tiresome journey.

The ministers, Mayor Peters, and a few reputable men were appointed to manage and decide what route to take. They drove many miles and met some difficulties. But through relying on the Lord, they found and decided on the best way for the migration to travel by land till the emigrants would reach the mighty waters.

This was not an easy matter. They had to make many

decisions, yet they had no modern communications. There were no telephones, computers, or fax machines, and mail service was slow and not dependable.

Meanwhile, they needed to attend a special church conference at Alexanderwohl. It took months for them to travel to various places to obtain full permission to emigrate from Russia. They needed to travel through different countries before boarding the ships. They had to arrange all this and calculate how much time it would take them to reach the different national borders.

Russia was in no hurry to release these Mennonites. People knew their land to be "the breadbasket of Russia," raising thousands of acres of red wheat. The czar and his government preferred to keep these hardworking people in their country.

The migration planning and moving was quite difficult for the well-talented men since they had taken hardly any interest in gathering information about foreign lands or even thinking about them. Many of their people did not know geography.

When the men chosen as delegates came back, they had much information to share throughout the many outlying settlements and villages.

Mayor Peters held a meeting in his house for the Heuboden folks. He explained the main plans and the dangers involved.

The mayor also reported: "At the conference a government official stood on the platform with a suggestion: 'Wouldn't it be better if we took the Bible out of our schools, especially if they are not able to read well? Would it be a sin if the Holy Bible would be replaced with Bible story books?'

"But," said Peters, "this was too ridiculous: Bible story books instead of the Bible, the true Word of God! No one considered this a worthwhile proposal."

The villagers anxiously asked, "What was the conference's decision?"

Peters told the alarmed folks how Ministers Ratzloff and Wedel of the Mennonites explained things to the officials: "On Mount Sinai God spoke the Ten Commandments to the children of Israel [Exodus 20]: 'I am the Lord thy God which brought thee out of Egypt, out of the house of bondage.

"'Thou shalt have no other gods before me. Thou shalt not

make unto thee any graven images. Thou shalt not bow down to them nor serve them.'

"And the Bible says, 'Teach a child the way of the Lord while he is in his youth, and he will not depart from it' [Proverbs 22:6]."

Dear readers: These Mennonites of Russia strongly believed these words and did not want to change their methods of teaching. They could not call it right to use Bible story books instead of the Holy Bible. It appears that Scripture was their only source of reading in school.

The one minister also told the officials: "The children are not committing a sin if they learn by memory from the Holy Word. The Word of God will last till the end of the world. We also hope to keep our method of school till the end."

The delegates attended another conference to obtain more orientation. When they returned, they thought that it was best not to give out all the information they had gathered since some of the settlements were becoming impatient.

The people wanted to know all the answers immediately and to know when this move to America would be. Many had not the least idea where America was or how far away. They did not learn of America in school. Indeed, they knew little of the big world outside their small villages.

The Mennonite leaders planned another meeting to decide who would go to America to search out a location suitable for the Mennonites. All of the most concerned men attended. They bowed their heads in prayer, asking the Lord's blessing and guidance in appointing the land scouts. With a vote they selected Uncle Heinrich Wiebe and Mayor Peters.

That evening at Isaac Harder's place, John said, "I think we have appointed two good men for this long voyage."

"I sure am curious about what they might find," responded Isaac. "This could take close to two years until we would be going. I pity the poor families who have hardly any money. Many cannot afford to migrate, but we must dare to help them, sharing our extra money.

"If all of us sell nearly everything we own, we might have enough so that all who wish to go along can join the migration."

By now Johann was ten years old. John and Tina had also become the parents of two little children. They were very special to his parents and to Johann, who enjoyed playing with them.

Still, Johann had a feeling that someone was watching him, but he didn't see the bad woman anymore. Every evening when he knelt in prayer beside his bed, he asked God in heaven to keep an extra watch over him so that he would be able to go along to America with his family.

"Please, God, if I cannot be with Mother Marie in heaven, let me go to a new land where no one will despise or mock me. I hope there will be no pigs in America, and nobody will call me 'hog rascal' any more. Oh, I hate to hear that name. God, did you know that Mother told me that if I pray and trust in you, you would protect me? I hope you did and will."

The next morning at breakfast, John and Tina discussed the migration being planned, but they said nothing about who all would be going. Johann sure hoped he would be included. His young mind could not grasp it all.

One day Johann was playing beside the big walnut tree when he heard a voice: "Hi, Johann," sniffed Abram Penner in tears. He told Johann that his mother had just whipped him again, and he had decided to visit Johann for some love and care.

Before long the two good friends were playing again. After supper they were slowly walking the village street and talking. They saw the herder coming with the cattle. All the children enjoyed trying to count them even if they could not count very far.

As the two boys leaned on the yard gate, looking closely at the cows, suddenly the herder yelled at them, "What're you two hog rascals doing here? You're scaring the cows." With his cattle-driving switch, he lashed a few hard strokes onto the boys. The cuts burned like fire. The boys cried bitterly, suffering severe pain. They could not imagine what they might have done wrong.

The herder, Mark's buddy, also could not accept the fact that this little boy was still alive. He was supposed to be dead.

☙ 18 ❧

Abandoned Again

One day the news spread through the villages. The land scouts had arrived back from the far-off land of North America.

Immediately folks wanted to hear the news. Mayor Peters was tired from the long voyage and wanted to rest a few days. But at least he said, "Yes, we found land with religious freedom granted to us—in Canada."

Two days later Heinrich Wiebe and Mayor Peters began holding meetings for the anxiously waiting villagers in three different settlements. They explained every detail to the sharp-eyed audience. Some could not grasp it. Most could not understand all the sacrifices, selling all they owned to raise money for the journey.

The children talked about the migration, too. It sounded exciting. Johann often told Abram Penner what all he would do in America. Abram had the impression that he would be going along too, but he had heard nothing from his parents.

Another year passed. Meanwhile, many parents and children were enthused about the proposal to migrate, but various concerns burdened the parents:

"We just do not have enough money to pay for this long voyage, but we cannot let our young boys be led astray by going to Moscow. Oh, this is a hard decision."

They prayed, "God, help us to decide what to do. Help us all to stay together."

"The children of Israel all left the land of Egypt together," someone reminded them, "and God led the way. Let's rely on God to help us through. There will be a way, I'm sure, if we trust and accept the Lord's guiding hand."

Nevertheless, some parents decided to take more time and see how this migration would go. Some did not want to sell everything they owned. They feared that they might arrive in an unknown land with nothing more than the clothes on their backs.

One evening after the three Derksen children were in bed, Tina approached her husband and suggested not taking Johann along to America.

"We simply cannot afford it," she said. "You know that the other two children are our very own, and Johann is not. The two small ones are not able to be without parents yet, but we could find someone to take Johann into their home. Surely he will not be left to wander alone."

"No, no, Tina," replied her husband. "You don't understand what Johann is to me. At the mayor's meeting on his first day of life, I promised that we would raise him to manhood. I can't let my boy here. I made this promise to God also, and I can't lie to God."

John walked back and forth in the kitchen with unbearable thoughts. Tina was not a woman like Marie had been, as he had discovered by now. She wanted to have her way.

With an aching heart and pleading eyes, he stood in front of his wife: "Well, then, we'll go without Johann if that's how it must be, but it will break his young heart again. He's already been through enough heartaches. This is just as hard for me to bear as it is for my son."

"Well, I have cared for him these few years now," said Tina. "Let someone else have their turn. My children come first. Actually, the mayor should pay us to keep him."

Since this decision was against his best choice, John was very sad. He could not face Johann about the decision, hoping that somehow a way would open up for Johann to go along. Both parents decided not to tell Johann about the matter till later.

One morning at the breakfast table a few days later, Tina said, "Now, children, we want to eat quickly and get ready for our sale. We are going to sell all the things we have except for a few clothes and precious items that we can carry. We need all the money from the sale to pay for our long journey. Today we will have the sale. So hurry up. It will be a big day."

Johann was very happy. He wanted to share his joy with his friend Abram Penner. And yet Abram was sad that his best friend would be leaving him.

All the villagers in Heuboden were moving except for thirteen families. Quite a few had a sale the same day as the Derksens. At the family's sale, Johann was quite helpful, bringing all the things he could find to raise as much money as possible for the journey.

Things sold fairly well except for the land. The Russians decided that they would not bid much for land since the Mennonites had to sell regardless of what price it would bring. These villagers were supposed to sell their land leases only to other Mennonites who stayed there or to Mennonites of another village or settlement.

The former mayors had made this agreement, which lasted until Mennonites failed to come forward to buy leases from the migrating villagers. The Mennonites who stayed got bargains in purchasing these leases, but when they migrated a year or so later, the Russians got great bargains in taking over the lands.

With great joy Johann waited for the final day of moving. The day before his family was to leave, he decided to go and bid good-bye to his friend Abram. Johann's parents had still not told him that they had decided not to take him along.

Abram shed tears when Johann left the house. Abram's stepmother was not at home, so the two boys had a good parting.

As Johann stepped outside the house, there stood the bad woman again, his real mother. She grabbed her son with both hands and threw him to the ground. He struggled with all his young energy to break loose from those strong, savage hands, but to no avail.

She had both her hands clenched around his neck and screamed right into his face: "Look at me one more time, and for the last time, you cunning child of mine."

He closed his eyes tight as he tussled to get away, but the woman was on top of him. Since she kept her grip at his neck, he could hardly breathe. He was so scared that he thought he must be dying. His agony distracted him so that he did not think of praying to God for help.

The evil woman now thought she would solve the major problem in her life by killing her unwanted son. But just then a man walking the village street yelled, "What goes on here?"

Immediately she let him loose and ran in haste through the Penners' mulberry bushes.

"What happened, little boy? Was that your mother?" asked the excited rescuer. "Are you okay?"

Johann got up and ran home without explaining things. The man walked on, not realizing how terrible the situation was.

Dear readers: For over ten years this woman bore her sin without repentance, living an unhappy life. Satan kept telling her that once the child was dead, she could repent. Esau also struggled with such thoughts for over twenty years, wishing to kill his brother, Jacob, but God protected him the same as he did Johann. Jacob's prayers changed his brother's heart. We have no evidence that this woman ever repented. How sad!

That evening Johann had another awful surprise when his stepmother said, "Johann, the way it looks since we had our sale, there just will not be enough money to pay for your fare to go with us to America.

"I know it's too bad, and I feel sorry for you, but you are better able to live with someone else than our two young children are. Actually, you are not our real son, you know. Someone will surely give you a home."

Dear readers: Can anyone imagine the grief this boy of ten and a half years had to suffer?

Speechless, Johann sat on the chair, his face buried in his hands, crying. He could not think that it was true; surely his dad would have told him. Johann knew that his stepmother did not love him as well as his mother Marie, who died when he was only seven years old.

The two younger children looked at their stepbrother and asked why he was crying. They were too young to understand.

Tina tried to soothe his heartache: "Someone will care for you. God will answer our prayers, and you must also pray. Maybe someone will pay for your fare in a year or two, and then we can all be together again."

At the family's sale, all the Derksen's belongings had been sold except for a few items they wished to keep—only what they could pack in their chest to take along. There was nothing left for Johann. He had not one item to call his own. There simply were no affordable toys or trinkets.

By that evening, everything was carefully packed, ready for the travelers to start out the next morning. After supper Tina put the children to bed early.

Tina was tired but could not sleep. She checked in the next room to see if Johann was asleep. As she sat beside the sad boy on the bed, she said, "Johann, can't you sleep? I'm very sorry to leave you here." The two hugged each other and cried.

Early the next morning, they ate breakfast in silence. Johann was not hungry for his mother's last meal.

"Johann, my dear, you should not be so distressed," said his father. "It makes it awful hard for me to leave this way, but we just have no extra funds to pay for another ship fare, and I don't want to borrow money because I don't know if I could ever pay it back.

"We might all die before we reach America. Furthermore, I would not know who to ask for money. No one has any to spare. The government would never loan us any money for this long journey.

"Go along the village street. Surely someone will take you into their home."

Sadly Johann sat out beneath the big chestnut tree. A few of those remaining in the village came to bid farewell to John and Tina. They saw the face of the forsaken boy and wondered if perhaps he was not allowed to go along. None of them could afford to open their door to care for him. A few thought he was more of a pain to the village than what he was ever worth, since he was not born of Mennonite folks.

At eight o'clock the immigration wagon, hitched to two horses, stopped at the Derksens' house. Their friends staying behind gave John, Tina, and the two little children a warm farewell handshake and wished them good luck and God's blessings on their long trek. They said, "We also might go to this new land someday."

Then John and Tina shook hands with their sorrowing son. The parents and the two innocent children hugged and kissed him and cried together. This parting was very hard for the father, but he relied on God's plan somehow to protect his son.

The men heaved the chest onto the wagon. The family of four climbed aboard. As Johann watched, he screamed and cried in anguish. Then the young boy slumped to the ground.

Tina saw him lying there. It was more than she could take, and so she turned to look the other way. John did not look back. He did not want to see possibly this last sad scene of his dear son, whom they had promised God and the mayor to raise to manhood, not only to age ten.

The team moved onward. Johann looked as long as he could, till the wagon moved out of sight as it passed along the street and over a rise.

Now the so-called orphan was alone. Can any of you readers imagine the grief this little boy endured? Can anyone understand the agony these poor parents endured on their long and dangerous voyage, crossing the rough and churning ocean waters while thinking of their adopted son left behind? No doubt they often wished to turn back and reverse this situation.

Surely no parents in our wealthy country of the United States would ever desert their once-well-loved children. Yet there are many ungodly parents who do not attend any religious services. Broken homes are the outcome, leaving innocent children to suffer while the parents spend their huge paychecks on "that which is not bread" (Isaiah 55:2). They are trying to enjoy life but are lost in sin. Take heart, young readers, and pray that this may never occur in your own family someday.

Johann cried till he had no more tears. He wondered where he might sleep that night. After a few long hours, two little girls walked by. They shared their love and pity with Johann, but they had no home to offer him.

His buddy Abram Penner came to see if Johann was still

there. Actually, it was not Johann's home any more. Abram encouraged Johann with love and urged him to trust that God would arrange for someone to let him sleep in their house.

Abram decided to go home and kindly ask his stepmother if Johann might live with them. "Mother, poor Johann has nothing to eat and has no place to sleep tonight. Please, may he come to live with us? We can't just leave him go hungry and live on the village street."

"No, no!" Helena erupted. "You won't bring that hog rascal on our property, let alone into my house. And don't say another word about him. Everyone knows why his parents left him behind. Now they are finally rid of him. He never belonged to our people anyhow. Picking him out of the hog pen only created problems."

As shadows from the westward arcing sun grew larger, the sad little boy wondered if he would ever see his parents again. His mouth was dry. He walked to the well to draw up water, but to his surprise, the pail and the rope were gone. His parched lips cried for water as he lay beside the well, abandoned.

☙ 19 ❧

Yet Another Mother

Daylight was fading as Mayor Peters walked the street to check if all went as the emigrants had planned. As he approached the Derksen home, he thought of these well-respected folks: "I will surely miss them, and perhaps someday we may live in the same settlement again. I'm not sure how long we will stay here, but my office as mayor means that I am entitled to stay here till nearly the last ones leave."

Suddenly he spied Johann by the well. "Johann, Johann, didn't you go along with your parents?"

At the sound of the voice, Johann slowly got up and saw Peters. "No," said the boy, crying, ready to accept any compassion he might receive. "They left me here. They said they had no money for my fare on the ship, whatever that means." He had no idea how a ship would look even though his father had tried to explain it.

"Where are you going to stay?"

"I have no place. Mrs. Penner won't let me stay at her house with my friend Abram."

"My, oh my, you poor fellow," said Mayor Peters as he reached out his hand. "You come and live with us. It's not right to let you here. I would have lent your father some money if I had known about this."

Johann clasped his little hand into the mayor's big one as they walked homeward.

"Mom, I brought John Derksen's son along home. I found him lying in their yard by the well. They left without him due to not having enough money for his ship fare. We'll keep him till we leave later."

"Oh my, oh my! Johann, you poor boy, are you hungry?" Susanna asked as she gave him a hug. "Did you have anything to eat since your parents left?"

"No, they took everything along, and I did not even have anything to drink," came his soft answer

Susanna made a warm supper for him, and he ate his meal with renewed hope, thinking that God had heard his prayers again. He wondered if his mother and father thought of him in the approaching dark night. While eating, he also thought of his loving mother Marie in heaven, knowing that she never would have left him behind. "God, find me a good mother again somewhere," he silently prayed.

The kitchen was nearly dark, and after a while he noticed that he was alone in the room. The mayor and his wife had gone into another room to discuss further about keeping the abandoned boy. "Sure, we'll just take him as our own child," agreed Susanna. "I'll never let a young homeless child on the street. We will certainly receive rich blessings from above, and I trust that God will reward us for it."

When they returned to the kitchen, Susanna asked, "Did you have enough?"

"Yes," and he cried a bit. "My head hurts."

"Yes, I reckon you are tired," she said with sympathy as she sat beside him and laid his head on her bosom.

Now his tears dripped upon her brown dress, and Susanna wept with him. She focused in her mind a picture of this forsaken boy lying by the well while his parents drove out of his sight, never to return.

"Come, Johann, I'll show you where you may sleep. Lie down and have a good sweet sleep. By tomorrow your headache should be gone.

"Now you are our little boy, and we will care for you as our own child. If things go as we plan, by next year we will go to America, too. You may go with us. We will never go without you. You may put your mind to rest on that. Now, good night. Sleep well."

"Good night," he sniffed. Her words were such a healing balm to his broken heart. Quietly he recited his short prayer, which his mother Marie had taught him, and then he fell asleep.

At eight o'clock that evening, this devoted wife of the mayor was washing the dishes from the boy's late supper when Frances

Dyck stepped inside without knocking and started talking.

"Good evening. My, you're still washing dishes! You must have had a busy day, I suppose, with all these folks moving. We stand around, watching them depart. Sort of a strange feeling, isn't it, saying good-bye forever?"

"Yes, the parting is hard," remarked Susanna, "especially for some who can't afford to take all of their family along."

"What do you mean?" asked Frances. "Surely no one left without their children!"

"Well, yes. This evening at dusk my husband found John Derksen's ten-year-old boy lying beside their well. I made a late supper for him, so that's why I'm still washing dishes. He's asleep now."

"You mean the little rascal is here?" Frances scolded. "I wouldn't accept him into my house. John and Tina were willing to care for him, as John promised. Remember the meeting here that night when he was found?"

These cruel words pierced into Susanna's heart like a dagger. She wished that she would not have mentioned anything about the forsaken lad. Just then her husband came inside and asked, "Is the little boy in bed by now?"

"Yes, he's sound asleep," reported Susanna.

"I told your wife that *I* wouldn't care for the boy," Frances said. "That's not your duty as a mayor. All this goes to prove that he made lots of problems for John Derksens. No wonder they left him here. It's no use to take along a child of unknown parents."

As Mayor Peters had heard, some villagers for a long time had assumed that Frances knew who Johann's unwedded father and mother were. This day her meddling was too much for the mayor. He was not a man to quarrel, but now he spoke directly to her face in a sharp tone: "Yes, I know you wouldn't care for the orphan boy. Your life has proved it.

"You and Mrs. Penner have created lots of trouble in our village the past years by your gossip and looking for trouble, meddling in other folks' matters where you have no business. The little boy did not create any problems."

Frances was surprised at this rebuke, and Susanna was glad to hear her husband tell Frances what's what.

“Yeah,” Frances shot back, “it seems that whenever there is a problem in the village, Helena Penner and I get blamed regardless of what the folks know about the situation. I guess it’s better to be taking the blame than to be blaming others.”

“Then quit blaming others and keep your pointed tongue where it belongs,” the mayor warned her. “All your hate does not belong among our people. We need true love and good common sense.

“You did not just happen to drop by,” snapped Mayor Peters as he opened the door to usher her out. “I sense that you knew all about it, that the boy is here with us. You only came to taunt and mock him and downgrade his parents.

“Now go home and think deeply over your ungodly life. We are always glad for visitors, but we do not acknowledge troublemakers. We welcome most any guests, but unfriendly ones are off our list. Good night.”

With anger in her heart, Frances left the house and went directly to Mrs. Penner, telling her every detail of what the mayor said. Helena’s ears were open to absorb every word.

“Wow, I never knew the mayor to be so forthright and harsh,” griped Frances. “Peters again called both of us troublemakers, wishing we would move away. He says that they are taking the boy along to America, but we both know that he’s only trying to put on a good show. I won’t believe it till I see it.”

“Me neither,” snickered Helena. “The boy never even had a proper last name. All I ever heard was Johann. There’s a good chance that they won’t be able to get immigration papers for him. I’m curious to see how their predicament turns out. Smart mayor he’ll be! Ha-ha, just watch him walk into a trap yet.”

Little Abram, Helena’s stepson, was in the adjoining room and heard the two women talking. He could not grasp it at all but gathered enough to know it was about his friend Johann. Abram cried into his hanky. Oh, it hurt him so. He only hoped that Johann could go along to America and live peacefully, starting life anew.

The next morning Johann was still nervous and uneasy over his parents leaving him behind. He could hardly eat breakfast.

“Johann,” said Susanna kindly, “you must eat. Don’t be

afraid of anything around here. Did you sleep well last night?"

"Yes, I did." He smiled a bit.

"This now is your home. I know you've had lots of sorrow and grief in your life. If you have any problems or don't feel well, tell me. I am your mother now."

Johann could feel her love as she laid her left hand on his shoulder. Being able to trust Susanna felt so good that he wanted to cry, but he had decided that he was too old to cry every time his feelings were stirred up.

Now, living with the mayor's family, he felt more protected than he had with his own parents. "Surely no one will hurt me on this property," he told himself.

After breakfast Johann wished to be alone and strolled out to the orchard. He sat down and leaned his back against a tree trunk. Thinking of all the carefree birds fluttering overhead, plus the nice warm sunshine and puffy white clouds above, he praised God for the love of another mother.

"Thank you, dear God in heaven, for giving me another mother." Now, with no one watching, he did not try to hide his tears of joy. His thoughts flowed with his tears as he remembered some of the heartaches he had already endured in his short life.

"Is this really my third mother? Will Susanna be my mother the rest of my life?" he wondered. "I surely hope she will be. I love her already the second day. It's more than I expected."

Actually, counting his birth mother and Sara Harder, who had nursed him, this was his fifth mother, but he was unaware of that. He had no idea that the evil woman who created lots of fear in him was his real mother. No responsible person wanted to tell him about his origin yet; it would not make sense to a ten-year-old.

In the peace of meditating, he was aroused by voices on the street. He made out two voices of women, familiar to him:

"Now, if he thinks we should move out of the village on account of that rascal, he's not thinking very well. We were here before he was. The village folks are so concerned about the boy."

"We'll see once next year if Peters takes him along to America. See how much mercy they have for him. If the mayor uses money collected from us village people, he'll be in trouble.

We'll keep on top of his records, for sure."

Johann could hardly believe what he heard. They showed no love at all for him, so he tried to wipe those rude words from his mind. "Do they know the mayor's character better than I do?" he asked himself. "This cannot be true that they would leave me here when they go next spring.

"Susanna says she's my mo-mo-mother." He stuttered in confusion. "Am I going to call her 'Mother'? Yes, if she loves me as her boy, I will call her 'Mother.'

"Such a sweet communion I had with God only a little while ago, and now I'm as confused as ever.

"Shall I go and ask Mo-mo-mother if she told me the truth? What shall I do? Just run off to another village where no one knows me? Then what would they call me? It's hard telling what. No, that would not be right. Maybe God would not care for me any more."

In his bewildered thoughts, he slouched to the ground, with his face on the earth. The sad ten-year-old prayed again, hoping that God would hear him.

"Please, God, way up in heaven, do not let them go and leave me here. Before my mother died, she said, 'If you pray to God, God will help you.' I think she said that she is going to heaven when she dies. I hope that she also tells you to watch over me so—"

Before he had finished, the two Peters daughters interrupted him. "Johann, why are you lying there like that? We wanted to play with you. We were looking all around for you."

Johann told them what he had heard.

"No, no, that's not true. You are our little brother now," they said.

Johann loved to hear them say "little brother." This was something new.

"When Father and Mother say you may go along to America, you can depend on that. Come, we'll go and ask Mother."

And so Susanna reassured him: "Johann, I don't want you to doubt my words. As I said, you do not need to be afraid. We are taking you along as well as all our three other children. We will pay your fare on the big ship. Just stay in the house or close to the other children if you are afraid." She gave him a motherly hug.

Now Johann was sure that he could trust this family. The children played together, and the girls watched closely to keep him safe while they walked to and from school. Johann's life was pleasant again as he helped with whatever work he was told to do.

Three months had passed since John and Tina, his former parents, had left. No one received any mail or word saying whether they or the others in their traveling party arrived safely in America—but this was not unusual.

Summer turned to fall. There was talk of voting in a new mayor if Mr. Peters should move in the spring. Yet most of the Mennonites of this village were thinking of going to America. They wished to hear news of those gone earlier. Even if there was no news, they still did not want to stay if their young men would have to go to Moscow.

One evening after sundown, Johann and his foster brother and sisters were playing hide-and-seek in the mayor's meeting room, part of the Peters house. Suddenly the dog barked a signal that someone was outside.

As Johann looked out the window, he saw a figure and screamed in terror. The girls and Mrs. Peters quickly came to his rescue. "Johann, what's wrong? Did you hurt yourself?"

He was trembling with fear and pointed out the window. All they saw was a woman creeping under the gate beyond the orchard. "What about the woman?" asked Susanna.

"It's that bad woman who wants to hurt me," he cried out.

"No, no, my child," reassured Susanna. "No bad woman or bad man will take you away from us. The big dog lying outside by the grape arbor will not let any stranger come around without barking a signal. He will not bite them, but they'll leave right away." Susanna sat the shaky boy down beside her on the bench.

"See, the dog with his sharp ears is another one of God's protecting ways. No one else heard her creeping around the house. But God also sends his protecting angels to watch over little children many, many times, to keep them from harm. You know that, don't you?

"My husband and I pray every morning and evening for our children's safety, and that includes you, too. Maybe you don't understand all the meaning of our prayers. Surely your mother taught you a prayer before she died.

"If you can't think quickly when you are in danger, just say the Lord's Prayer, 'Our Father which art in heaven. . . .' God hears every prayer. Even if you just say, 'Lord, help me,' God will take care of you."

☙ 20 ❧

Off to Canada

The trees were bare as the cold wind whistled through the village of Heuboden. The cattle inside the small crude barns were cold. Winter had set in earlier than usual, and the folks were not yet prepared for it.

The north wind blew for three weeks, bringing deep snowdrifts. It was hard for any horse pulling a sleigh since there were no snowplows anywhere.

The children did not attend school in the depths of winter. It was too cold in the schoolhouse. For safety from the cold, the folks did not venture outside more than necessary.

Johann and the children did the chores because their father, Mayor Peters, had many tasks in arranging for the migration in the coming spring.

When the weather permitted, he drove to the other settlements to help them plan for moving. Often people came to his house to lay plans for the journey to Canada, in North America. They asked all kinds of questions and needed his counsel. Many could not decide what they needed to sell.

Mayor Peters reminded them to give thought to providing enough money to pay their ship fare. Some sold practically everything rather than stay in Russia. Many packed only one small chest. Some only took one set of clothes along. Others packed a chest or two and a few bags.

While the cold wind was blowing outside, Mrs. Peters decided to sew a few new sets of clothing for her family "Next year we'll be busy pioneering in America. We will surely not have time to sit down and sew clothes," she told herself.

She made Johann a new shirt and trousers. He was a very happy boy, going to America in new clothes!

Johann again decided to visit his friend Abram Penner before they started off. He showed him his new clothes. Johann told

Abram what all he looked forward to doing and seeing on the big ship. Both boys were so engrossed in this adventure, hoping that Abram's parents would also go along.

"Hey, you cranky hog rascal, get outta here," yelled Abram's mother. "Go out to the hogs, where you belong."

So Johann left without saying good-bye to his dear friend. With this sad parting, their friendship was forever put on hold.

Mayor Peters nailed together a few chests, and Johann enjoyed helping. In them they packed what was needed on the long voyage, along with a few tools to start off in the distant land.

Frances Dyck and Helena Penner were glad to see this righteous mayor move out of sight. Little did they realize that their problems were not over. Another mayor was appointed.

"Tomorrow morning the Peters family will be leaving," said Frances. "We'll watch to see if the boy will be going along."

As the evening shadows lengthened, the Peters family had everything sold except what they had packed into the chests. Their land and their buildings were no longer theirs. Everyone was tired.

Many friends came during the sale day to wish them well, and the good-bye hugs and handshakes were final. People shed some tears. The family sold the chairs, tables, beds, and furniture. The tired folks sat on the chests and the floor.

Johann thought, "Will I ever see this homestead again? Will I now be rid of that evil woman?" He trusted God not to let her go to America and ever trouble him again.

A few families of their best friends came at dusk, shared some words of blessing, and sang a parting hymn with them:*

Lebt wohl!

O Scheidestunde, ernste Stunde!
Denn Scheiden wird dem Herzen schwer,
Weil wir zum engsten Liebesbunde
Uns einten täglich mehr und mehr;
Es war so segensreich, so süß
Was uns der Herr genießen ließ.

---

* Author unknown (1835?), translated by S. David Garber (2005). Seelenfreund, "Soul Friend," refers to Christ.

Wie oftmals waren wir beisammen
Gescharet um das Wort des Herrn!
Wir sangen Lieder seinem Namen
Und beugten Herz und Knie so gern.
Da waren wir so klein, so bloß
Und doch im Herrn so reich und groß.

Wie fühlbar war uns oft der Segen,
Wie liebreich uns der Heiland nah!
Die Herzen schlugen ihm entgegen
Wenn er so freundlich auf uns sah.
Wir waren um den Seelenfreund
So oft geschart, so oft vereint.

Nun aber ist es Zeit zu scheiden.
Wir scheiden, doch nicht hoffnungslos:
Nach dieses Lebens kurzem Leiden
Wird in der ew'gen Liebe Schoß
Da unsre Seligkeit erhöhn,
Daß wir uns fröhlich wiedersehn.

Lebt wohl, lebt wohl! ihr teuren Herzen
Und bleibt dem Heiland alle treu!
Der Mann der Liebe und der Schmerzen
Uns allerorten nahe sei!
Lebt wohl, vom Argen unberührt,
Bis der am Kreuz zusammen führt!

Farewell!

Oh, hour of parting, solemn hour!
For parting breaks the heart so sore,
Because our love binds us with pow'r,
Unites us daily more and more.
Such sweet, rich blessing, what a treasure,
The Lord allows us with no measure.

How often were we gathered near,
Together round God's Word, so free,
And in his name sang hymns so dear,
So gladly bent our heart and knee.
We were so bare, of low estate,
And yet in God so rich and great.

How oft we felt the blessing rest,
How near to us the Savior's love!
For Him our hearts beat welcome best
When He smiled on us from above.
We round our Soul Friend gathered nigh,
So oft as one, to Him we'd cry.

Yet now to part cuts like a knife.
We part, but not with loss of hope:
Beyond brief sufferings of this life,
Eternal love will give us scope
And heighten bliss in God's domain,
That we with joy will meet again.

Farewell, farewell! our friends so dear,
And to the Savior still be true.
The Lord of love and pain be near
Us every place that we may view.
Farewell, be safe from evil weather,
Till He on th' cross leads us together.

Warm-hearted people squeezed a few tears out of their eyes. After the farewell song ended, the group fell on their knees in prayer, led by an older man, asking God's blessings upon their journey. He also prayed that the Peters family would care for Johann in the new land, and that they would never cast him away.

Johann's young mind no longer questioned whether he was included in the voyage. He knew he was going along as part of the Peters family.

When everyone had left, the family finally laid down on a few blankets to sleep. It was late, and everyone was tired.

The next morning they heard a knock on the door. They had overslept. The driver of the wagon was there, surprised to find them still asleep. "Come on! I thought you folks were going to America."

Everyone hustled out the door without breakfast. They had a few apples packed in a bag, to eat later. The cold coffee jug went along. After the men loaded the two chests, the six family members climbed aboard.

The wagon moved onward to pick up two more families. Johann sat on the back of the wagon, looking over the village for the last time. He mind roamed through some sad memories of his boyhood as he scanned places where he had hidden from his foe.

"I hardly dare think that my problems are over, but I sure am glad to get out of this area," he muttered to himself. He clasped both his hands on the wagon for total security, yet wished to relax.

With one more look at the hills of Russia, Susanna wept, realizing that she was leaving many good friends behind. She hoped that they would migrate to America someday, too.

Johann thought the driver should move faster, not understanding the weight on the wagon. By mid afternoon the wagon rolled into the train station. Johann's young eyes looked everywhere. Such huge buildings he had never seen or imagined. The streets were full of people. The big trains were truly amazing to the eyes of the four Peters youngsters.

"Johann," called his mother. "We're here. Let's get off the wagon."

The driver shouted, "All chests and bags off. Everyone off the wagon. I gotta keep moving. It'll be long after dark till I get back. Seventy-five cents for each family. Pay now." And then, after collecting his money, he was gone.

Mayor Peters was in charge of the many folks' identifications and needed to arrange and guide the group. At dusk he sat on a chest and sighed: "My, I'm tired. I sure hope that everything's taken care of so we won't have any problem getting on the train with all these different families."

Almost all the ones moving out of Heuboden sat together on their chests at the train station, eating their supper of dried fruit and bread. The water at the station tasted bad.

That night, Johann could hardly sleep due to all the new excitement. Before dawn the next morning, the sleepy travelers heard a shrill whistle: "Whoooooo-ooooh. Whooooooo." Everyone was on the move as the train pulled in at the station and the iron wheels came to a halt.

Johann saw faces in every window of the train. The side door of a train car opened. Long lines of dirty and weary people ascended the three steps. They were lugging brown handbags, and children were hanging on to a parent's hand.

"All aboard, ladies and gentlemen," shouted the conductor as he waved his hand. Men shoved all the chests into the luggage car. Johann could hardly wait to climb aboard. "Johann," said Susanna Peters as he clutched her skirt, "we must wait in line." Then after a bit she added, "Now we will go."

Walking down the center aisle, they passed seats on either side, dusty and unclean. Before they were seated, the train began moving, and the little boy clung to seatbacks to keep his balance.

"Look, mother, the houses are moving."

"No, my darling, they are not moving. *We* are moving. Hear the wheels clanging?"

The conductor, sporting his uniform with bright polished buttons, was collecting the tickets and captured Johann's attention. He sat tightly against his mother for better security. Train riding was all new to him, and he could not relax. He was asking many questions in a low tone. Susanna also had never ridden on a train in all of her fifty-two years.

Day and night the steel wheels rolled northwestward. All the cars were full, with some emigrants standing in aisles and children sitting on the floor. As time passed, they made new friends. Grandparents, husky strong farmers, childbearing women, families with children as many as nine, tall grown boys and girls—all were heading for a new homeland in North America. All were leaving their birthplaces in Russia, never to return.

The train stopped at many stations. The crew would attach more cars while the passengers jumped off for water. Some washed clothes in a stream; others found water for tea and coffee.

They saw rich, dark Russian soil, green fields of growing wheat, last summer's partially fed haystacks, buildings with straw-thatched roofs. A few windmills with whirling blades dotted the countryside. And in the background they could see green forests and mountains.

After two days and one night on this rough, bouncing train, everyone was tired and restless. They were occasionally munching on their meager supplies of dried meat and fruit, and no one was gaining weight, but rather the opposite. The dry black bread and the strong coffee reduced the pleasure Johann had anticipated.

The mayor had reminded their group that this would be a hard ride, sleeping in an upright position for fourteen days and nights while traveling into Western Europe. They passed through Aleksandrovsk (= Zaporizhzhya), Kharkov, and Kiev, then crossed the Dnieper River. When they reached Poland, they had to change trains. After passing through Krakow, the train entered Germany and finally reached the port of Hamburg.

"Whooooooh-whoooooh-whooo whoooooh." Day and night this sound was familiar. Finally the weary-faced travelers slept without hearing the steam whistle. Children and grown-ups became irritated in these stuffy, foul-smelling cars. Water was always scarce. The unkempt and reeking smell of the toilet room presented a bad odor halfway to the front of the car. There were no flush toilets anywhere.

The spring landscape helped to keep their spirits alive. As possible, Mennonite groups shared morning and evening devotions in these rattling, swaying third-class cars, not called coaches. Every day they sang together, to lighten their spirits. The changing scenery was the most interesting part of the trip.

The healthy people became somewhat adjusted to their sitting position, but the older and weaker ones were nearly exhausted. While thinking of the rocking ship on the long sea voyage, some wished that they had stayed in Russia. For most of these emigrants, the travel experience brought a mixed feeling of adventure and hardships, but mostly the latter.

With the group standing at the harbor, their little minds tried to grasp how the mighty ships would glide on the ocean waters. Mayor Peters was inside the shipping office, arranging all the passports for their group to sail across the Atlantic Ocean.

Johann held tightly on to his mother's hand as they ascended the gangplank onto the 150-foot-long ship. Men carried the heavy wooden chests onto the ship, which was soon loaded with Russian Mennonites and a crew of sailors.

The ship left the dock at Hamburg and floated down the Elbe River and into the North Sea. It passed through the English Channel alongside the Netherlands, Belgium, and France. The choppy waters rocked the crude vessel. Everyone preferred to stand on the deck till dark, so as not to miss any waterfront scenes.

At night they all were trying to get some sleep on the bunk beds. This seemed like luxury compared to the swaying train seats. The first night was very foggy. Johann jumped out of bed at the loud boom of the foghorn at midnight. At sundown the next day, they waved good-bye to the European shores as they rocked up and down on the great Atlantic.

The main food was raw and cooked cabbage, potatoes and dried bread, tea and coffee. Some days they did not eat much food because many were seasick. They threw not one morsel of food to the crying seagulls swooping downward. The only scraps the birds found were what the passengers spewed over the side. The drinking water tasted awful, causing more sick stomachs.

Long before they came to the end of the bouncing sea voyage, many fingers were scratching their itchy bodies because of lice infesting the bunks.

Water spraying twenty feet out of the ocean proved to be from whales exhaling through their blowholes. The passengers feared for their lives and wished to be on dry Canadian ground. For days they saw nothing but green shadowy water and white-capped waves, plunging their ship twenty feet down and then back up again. It became monotonous. But they clung to the hope of a new dawning of life.

The sun warmed their bodies. The half moon and stars told them that the same God was still protecting them. They trusted that he would give the captain wisdom to steer the laden vessel on the proper path through the dark and stormy nights. They had no way of knowing their direction except that every morning, light dawned across the ocean from the ship's rear, revealing their westward heading. Otherwise, they had no proof since they lacked the skill of telling directions by the sun and the stars.

After nineteen days, a sailor shouted from the crow's nest, "Land ahoy, land ahoy." They were approaching the shore of Newfoundland, on which he had spotted a lighthouse. Everyone scrambled onto the deck, waiting, straining their weary eyes. They could see nothing but water, but their trust did not fade.

Mayor Peters had seen the new land a year earlier, and the Russian Mennonites believed his report and had faith in his words. Now Peters asked the captain for his telescope. His searching eye could now see the North American shores.

Curious Johann wanted to look too but could not see any land. "All water, no land," he reported.

"You didn't hold the telescope at the right angle." Mr. Peters smiled and helped him aim the instrument.

The captain laughed. "If you would have crossed the ocean as often as I have, Buddy, you could see land. We'll get there."

At daybreak everyone saw land on the western horizon. Now they could finally realize how slowly the ship moved across the ocean. It took another night until the grey vessel floated in the St. Lawrence River. By the next dusk it arrived in Quebec City.

The immigrants had never seen city lights before. What an interesting country! The excitement kept many of them awake all night even though the sea was finally calm.

The next morning Mayor Peters walked down the gangplank onto dry land again, like a mother hen leading her brood. The whole group cheered. Canadian officials escorted them into the immigration offices. Never before had they seen such large buildings. Their eyes took in the sights all around.

"Whoooohooo-whoooo-whoooohoooo" came the sound of the train whistle as the happy group walked toward the big red station. They could hardly wait to climb aboard. "Where is our new home, Mother?" asked Johann. "In a big house?"

"No, no, Johann," she replied with a laugh. "We must go on a long train ride yet. This may take three or four days longer, maybe a week."

Johann could not understand. He thought that when they got off the ship, that would be the end of the long journey.

Aboard this train and traveling along, they noticed better riding than in Russia. Food tasted different and better in this new land. Their hopes were high. Yet the thick black smoke of the steam engine crept inside the coaches whenever they opened the windows for fresh air, coating the passengers with black dust. There were no air conditioners or modern washrooms.

To follow the most convenient route, the train ducked into the United States. Finally, on the afternoon of the fourth day, they reached Moorhead, along the Red River in Minnesota. Here the tired and smoke-blackened immigrants got off the train and stepped aboard a fine-looking steamship. Now they could wash their itchy bodies again.

Heading north, downstream on the Red River, this seemed like a pleasure ride compared to crossing the ocean, where they could see only sky and water and birds. Here green forests were on either side of the river, with deer and geese plus a few houses.

Johann was sitting on the deck, enjoying every moment and asking his third adoptive mother all kinds of questions. The ship passed Grand Forks and then just north of Pembina, it crossed the international line into southern Manitoba, Canada.

The ship made a turn close by the river's edge, beneath low-hanging branches. Mayor Peters quickly grabbed the guardrail to avoid being thrown overboard and taking a cold bath. "Hang on, Dad," yelled Johann.

Rounding a curve on the Red River, they saw a clearing of farming ground near Niverville. Off in the distance were a few small, crude buildings, which Russian immigrants had built less than a year earlier.

"Here we are, brothers and sisters," announced Mayor Peters as the ship moved slowly along the riverbank. The captain found a place to lay out the gangplank. "All of our group, take your chests and bundles off the ship. This will be our new homeland."

As the crew lifted the gangplank, the steam whistle echoed "Wheeeeeeee-wheeee-wheeeeeeep" across the flat valley. They all waved good-bye to the captain and crew as the steamer moved on toward Winnipeg.

Johann could not figure out where everyone would live, since they could see only one home.

"So, this is where our long journey has ended, my friends," proclaimed Mayor Peters to the group of confused-looking people.

"Let us all fall onto our knees with clasped hands toward heaven, and thank our heavenly Father for his guiding hand and protection on our long journey."

As everyone kneeled on the thick grassy sod, the one minister among the group led in a prayer:

"Heavenly Father, we thank you for the unbounded love and mercy that you have bestowed upon us during our long voyage. We thank you that we did not need to throw one dead body into the mighty restless sea, and that you have brought us safely to a new land, where we may still worship the same God as our forebears did in the old country."

At the minister's invitation, the whole group joined in praying the Lord's Prayer: "Our Father which art in heaven . . . Thine is the kingdom, and the power, and the glory, for ever. Amen." Then together they sang:*

Nun danket alle Gott
mit Herzen, Mund und Händen,
der grosse Dinge tut
an uns und allen Enden;
der uns an Leib und Seel
von früher Kindheit an
un zählig viel zu gut
bis hieher hat getan.

Now thank we all our God
With heart and hands and voices,
Who wondrous things hath done,
In whom His world rejoices;
Who, from our mothers' arms
Hath blessed us on our way
With countless gifts of love,
And still is ours today.

Susanna sat on one of their wooden chests, her tired body slumped forward, her face buried in both hands, crying.

* By Martin Rinckart (1636), translated by Catherine Winkworth (1858).

"Mother," exclaimed Johann, "why are you crying?"

"Oh, Johann, this looks so hopeless, coming to a new land, with no home to live in. Who will take us in? You've had enough hardships in your young life." She dried her tears on her apron.

"Come now, we're here, and we must keep our heads high," urged her husband. "It looks difficult to me, too. But we need to have courage and struggle to make a place for ourselves.

"I don't know where we could find a better location. We'll have to build homes the same as our ancestors did in Russia after they left the Netherlands and later left the Danzig area of Prussia. Remember, we decided this long trek would be rewarding in the end—rather than have our young men sent off for military training."

"Yes, yes, I know," Susanna said. "But it still looks like endless toil to me. Johann, you don't realize all the hard work involved in cutting down trees in the wilderness and building a house and barn."

"But at least I can enjoy my life here without someone trying to hurt me," replied Johann. "This looks very interesting."

The group walked to the town of Niverville, where an official signed their immigration papers. Here they stayed a few days while Mayor Peters rode to Vollwerk (= Reichenback, or Mitchell), where some had settled a year earlier.

"Hello, hello, Mr. Peters," welcomed the local Mennonites. "My, it's good to see you again. So you made it safely across the deep waters of the North Atlantic. Tell your group that we have room in our houses till they can build their own homes."

In a few days, they were settled. The men began cutting trees and building crude one-room cabins.

Whole families worked hard—men, women, and children—hopefully pioneering in this Manitoba colony. They purchased oxen to plow the tough prairie sod. They planted seeds to keep them from starving. They trusted God that the crops would grow on the virgin soil.

Johann liked to help his father with the plowing, walking along and guiding the oxen with a stick. The flies made the oxen mean and nasty, somewhat disobedient. A few times they ran off. But through it all, Johann grew to be a strong, hardworking lad.

ᏨᏨ 21 ᏇᏇ

The Girlfriend

That first summer the Peters family plus many more built their homes, and in time the village was prospering. They were living with much the same customs as in Russia.

In the year 1880 Johann turned eighteen. He enjoyed farming and developed a lot of skill by training his team of oxen so well. They obeyed him by word, so he did not need to use a stick or reins. He would let them graze on unfenced prairie land.

One day Dad Peters said, "Keep the oxen in the barn overnight, Johann. I want to head for Winnipeg at four o'clock tomorrow morning. It's too hard to find them in the dark." So Johann tied them in the barn that night.

Mr. Peters' office as mayor did not expire as long as he was healthy and managed his affairs properly. Early that morning, three of the men started for Winnipeg on business. This was a slow trip that they took a few times a year to obtain supplies.

As they returned through swampland, the wagon bogged down to the axle. The oxen were sunk in deep mire, and the wagon was stalled. The men had to unload many items to get the two-horned beasts started again. This was strenuous labor for the barefooted Mennonites, wading in muck halfway to their knees.

"We must find another route to Winnipeg," groaned Mr. Peters as they reloaded the supplies again. "The next time we'll take some young, strong boys along. There is too much swampland along the Red River."

After that experience, Johann and a few young friends went along to Winnipeg.

One day Mr. Peters said, "Well, Johann, you are at the age when you should be thinking of becoming a church member. Are you willing to join with the other youth this summer? They start the instruction classes in three weeks."

"Yes, Father, I've been thinking about it, and I wish to be a church member in the same congregation where you are."

"All the members must have their names registered in my record book," Mr. Peters reminded him. "As you may know, you are given a choice of three family names. A year ago I told you about your first days on earth, when your one mother Marie Derksen lifted you out of the hog pen, saving your young life.

"Sara Harder kept you alive by nursing you till you could eat bread and live with the Derksens. So in Heuboden we had listed you as Johann Derksen. After Marie died, John Derksen married Tina, who became your mother. Then Susanna and I brought you along from Russia to Canada as part of our family.

"So now, which family name do you prefer?"

The young lad was confused, had no answer, and asked for time to think things over. He had always signed his name as Johann. He thought, "Could this cause a hardship in my life if I make a wrong decision now?"

He went out to the barn, beside the oxen, and prayed for wisdom. He could not decide on his own. After he searched his heart and thought deeply about the good and faithful parents he now had, he decided to write his name as Johann Peters.

The family was at the table when at length Johann came back to the house. They sensed that this decision was very hard on him.

"I want to be Johann Peters," he declared as he stretched forth his hand to his father. He broke into tears and cried for a while, thinking of the four women who had cared for him as their son, in addition to the woman who gave him birth.

Have any of you readers ever had four people you called Mother, but still none of the four was your birth mother? Actually, Johann saw all five face to face, but he did not know that the one who nearly choked him to death was the mother who gave him birth. It's good he didn't know that.

This single woman could hardly forget her oft-regretted youthful sin, which plagued her throughout her entire life. The devil would not release her weary mind. She wished that she could have loved this boy. Now he was reassured of having a better life in a far-off continent.

The day Johann was baptized, he felt a big responsibility to try his best to be a faithful Christian church member. He vowed that he would cast his lot with Christ and so live until death.

"Trust in the Lord and acknowledge him in all your ways," counseled the preacher. "I wish for you all the everlasting salvation of our Lord Jesus Christ. Remember, young folks, we look for the good fruits of good deeds. You are called to this way of life, and you may produce these good fruits through earnest prayers and faithful obedience to God."

Now Johann felt a sincere security that God would protect him from any harm. Eventually he began looking around for a life companion, someone to be his wife.

At age twenty-five in 1887, he took full responsibility for his father's farm, plowing with two oxen, planting, and harvesting. He would chop wood for winter heating and for cooking meals in the summertime. In this new land of Canada were plenty of trees.

Mayor Peters still had many responsibilities to handle, as in the old country. So he offered Johann a portion of the income from the farm. Johann saved every bit for his future years.

"Where shall I farm if I decide to get married someday?" he asked his father. "Your other son is able to do the farming here. What if I buy a farm on my own?"

"Sure, that's okay," answered his foster dad. "You did so much work for us that to be fair we must help you get started on your own."

Many of the Russian folks from Heuboden had settled east of the Red River. Johann had heard that some Mennonites were buying land and starting to break sod in the Plum Coulee area, west of the Red River but still in Manitoba.

There he purchased a tract of land, built a home, and moved into it by himself. Now he was on his own, and life seemed to be exciting and fulfilling. Johann worked long days, farming, building, and preparing a home. He wished for a helper, someone to make meals for him.

Johann asked his best helper, the Lord, to guide him in seeking a companion whom he could trust to share his life. He knew of an Abram Falk family that had three daughters, and one was deaf.

On a beautiful Sunday morning after a hurried breakfast, he rode one of his two farm horses to Kronsgart, twelve miles away. Along the way he passed a few sod houses and also some roughly boarded ones. Riding bareback, the sweating horse made his pant legs wet. A few times Johann dismounted and let Jim eat the prairie grass.

As he rode along, he meditated about the future. "Come on, Jim. Let's get moving." He was not used to riding such a distance. Finally they came to a creek. Johann got off and let the thirsty horse drink. "I wonder how deep the water is," he said as he stared ahead. "We'll give it a try, Jim," and he mounted again.

Splash, splash, splash—the water came up to Jim's neck. "This is deep enough," he muttered as he pulled up his bare legs, getting on his knees on Jim's back to keep from having soaked pants.

When he arrived at what he thought was the Falk home, he hoped it was the right place. Johann met Abram in the yard, hitching a horse to the little wagon. Two daughters quickly ran for the house after seeing the handsome boy astride the horse. This was an unusual event. They hid at the corner of the house, peeping at him.

"Good morning, Abram. A nice day," Johann recognized and greeted him.

"Good morning. Are we getting a visitor?" Abram replied. After a hearty handshake, he asked, "How did you know the way to get here, young man? A person can soon get lost in this sparsely settled area."

"Oh, I just looked around," Johann said. Actually, he had been listening for information about these Falks and their girls.

"Mother and I are going to visit the sick neighbor lady, though it is quite a distance. There are no close neighbors around here, as you know. However, you may visit with the girls till we get back!"

As Abram drove out the lane with his wife, he said, "I think that is the son of Mayor Peters. I met him with Peters once. He's the boy they brought along from Russia. Remember? I told you about him once."

"What's he after? Our girls, you think?" she asked.

"I dunno. Any objections? He looks like a nice boy."

"I have no problem. Do you?"

Johann stood in the yard, watching the wagon disappear. At first the two girls were too shy to go and meet him.

"Trienchen," said Anna, "you go out and tell him he may feed his horse in the barn."*

"And when he has tied him, then what shall I say to him?"

"Nothing. If he stays standing outside, that's okay. If he asks to come along into the house, that's good too. We'll visit with him in the kitchen."

With a blushing face, Trienchen walked over to Johann and said, "Hi. I don't know you, but you may tie your horse in the barn and feed him if you wish. He probably is tired too and needs to rest."

She walked with him to the barn but felt a bit uncomfortable to be so close to the good-looking stranger. As Johann came out of the stable door, he glimpsed a full picture of her rosy young face, with golden braided hair hanging behind her ears.

Trienchen felt so shy that she lowered her deep blue eyes to the ground, not knowing what to say.

"May I have a drink of water?" came the timid voice of Johann.

Now Trienchen sighed with inner relief since this was a familiar matter. "Sure. Come along in. Do you want a cup of coffee, too?"

"Well, yes, but I sure don't want to disturb your Sunday rest. You weren't expecting company, were you?"

"Well, no. Are you planning to go further?" Trienchen asked. "We'll make dinner for you if you wish. Sit down. I reckon you're tired. How far do you live from here?"

"Twelve miles south, in the Plum Coulee area. It's such a nice day that I thought I'd go for a ride."

After the cool drink refreshed Johann's thirsty body, he looked her straight in the eyes and said, "Thanks."

And she smiled.

Her two sisters had gone into the other room.

---

* Trienchen, a nickname of endearment, means "little Katharina."

Trienchen made hot coffee, and they sat at the kitchen table across from each other.

"Well, how's it going here in your area?" asked Johann.

"Oh, we get lonesome. There are not many people in this wide-open country. How about where you live?" Her shyness was diminishing a bit.

"Not a whole lot of people where I live, either, but in a few years more will come, we hope. Folks are interested."

The big wall clock chimed three times. It looked like the same clock his father John Derksen had in Russia.

"You might stay for supper. Sister Anna and I are used to cooking," she informed him.

After they were done eating, Johan and Trienchen sat together, visiting again. The dog barked. Johann looked out the window and saw the parents coming in the lane. He grabbed his hat. "Good-bye, Trienchen. Thanks for the meal."

He met her father, Abram, in the barnyard, and he said, "Well, are you leaving? I did not mean to chase you off. How are the folks at home?"

"Ah, I-I live alone since I bought my own farm," he replied in a timid voice.

"You're the mayor's son, right?" asked Abram.

"Ah, y-y-yes." Johann did not really know how he should answer since he knew that Peters was not his birth father.

While Johann mounted his horse to ride bareback, Abram invited him to come again. As he rode out the lane, he looked back once more. His new girlfriend waved her hand from the yard, and he waved back, so much as to say, "I'll see you later."

Johann let his horse walk for a while as he thought of his precious visit with this strange girl, whom he had never seen before. His mind wandered back to the past and far into the future.

Later in the evening, Trienchen overheard her parents talking seriously in the bedroom. She was curious and listened and heard them mention Johann's name. "I can hardly believe that this is the little boy who was found out in the cold hog pen by a Derksen woman," said Abram.

"What are you talking about?" piped up Elizabeth, his wife.

"Don't you remember that story about a little baby back in

the early sixties? Nobody knew who his parents were. A young couple without children raised him. I can't remember everything, but there was quite some confusion in Heuboden for a while."

Trienchen's ears had heard more than she wished. She did not sleep much that night. "Should I ask him about this the next time he comes?" she wondered. "Surely not all that Father said is true."

After some thought, she decided not to bring up the subject right away. It might make him feel inferior.

ଓ 22 ଛ

Johann's Second Visit

In her daily routine of helping her parents on the farm, Trienchen constantly thought about the young man Johann, with whom she longed to have further friendship. She wished to know more of what she had heard her father say about him.

A week passed, with no news. She did not want to ask her mother, and her mother did not wish to share such a subject with her young daughter. She sensed that her daughter was not as usual since that youth had appeared.

Another week passed. On Sunday afternoon Trienchen wished to be alone, to cipher out her thoughts through meditating. She walked down by the creek and sat on the bank, watching the fish swimming by. "Nature is free of problems," thought the confused girl.

She pondered what her future might someday be with this young man. Suddenly she saw Johann on the opposite bank, standing beside his sorrel horse.

"Hi! Did I scare you?" asked Johann.

"Yes, you did, but I was in deep thoughts, wondering when you would come again. Even my dad mentioned something this morning, thinking that you might come today. Did he know it? Come on over to this side."

Johann mounted Jim and rode through the shallow stream. As he got off the horse, she reached out her hand. "My, it's good to see you again. I was so lonesome. Maybe you sent me a letter, but we don't get any mail unless we go to town and pick it up—which happens about once a month. It's too far, you know."

"The two sat on the bank for a long time, talking, getting acquainted, sharing their memories of childhood days. They felt each other's love, but Trienchen kept pulling off small blades of grass to cover her shyness. She did not know how to approach the subject of his childhood.

He told her of his rough school days and how the teacher treated him. They both shed tears of sorrow when he recounted the death of his mother Marie. They also cried together over how his next mother told him that they had no money to pay his fare on the ship, and his parents drove off, and he had no home.

"My, oh my, how could they do that to you?" She laid her hand on his shoulder. "Did you say you were only ten years old? Where are John and Tina now? Are they living in your area?"

"I haven't seen them for three years, since they moved further west," he said. "My dad John wanted to accept me, but Mother Tina was more the opposite. I think she could hardly face the fact that someone else cared more for me and brought me along to Canada a year later.

"I think her conscience plagued her more than she reckoned it would. Before they were married, she had promised John that she would always treat me as her own son. After we met in Canada again the first time, Dad John told me it was awfully hard for them in crossing the ocean and not knowing if someone gave me a home.

"He wished he could turn back to bring me along. He told Mother Tina that it was not right in the eyes of God to let an innocent, homeless child suffer so."

"Who were your grandparents?" asked Trienchen.

"Ah, uh, I-I don't really know," stammered Johann. "I never met them. I assume that they were dead before I was born or lived in a far-off village." This was a question he had not thought of. Really, he didn't know them, and he never knew the kind of love that grandparents give.

"Were you born in the Heuboden village?" asked Trienchen. She was still curious to know more about what her father had said, whether he really had been found in the hog pen.

Johann was running out of answers. "I think it was close to Mother Marie's Uncle Isaac Harders," he answered with a far-off look. "Well, I think it's best that I feed my horse before I start for home," he said as he broke off the sore subject.

Actually, Johann did not wish to tell her all the true facts of being found in the hog pen. He often wondered why

people made nasty remarks about him being a hog boy. His mother Marie knew it would nearly ruin his young mind if he dwelled on the horror of such stark truth.

My personal feeling is that parents should explain the hard truth of any such happenings involving their children when they become adults. They should relate these things in a loving and sincere Christian attitude before the child hears it from others.

As the pair of friends approached the farm buildings, Elizabeth looked out and remarked to her husband: "I see the young man Johann is here with Trienchen again. What if she finds out about his background? Should we tell her at the beginning of their friendship? It worries me since no one has any trace of his birth parents. What if he would turn out not to be a faithful husband?"

"Well, I don't think we should discourage her," declared Abram. "I trust that the Lord is leading him here. If our son would have a decent girlfriend, would you call it right if someone would speak evil of him or his parents?

"If he is man enough to own a farm, his reputation speaks for itself. Let him tell her sometime if he wishes to share it. Let's pray for him instead of worrying. We dare not judge any children according to their parents."

Johann and Trienchen strolled into the house and visited with her parents for a while. Then he said, "Well, it's best that I head for home. I'll be back again in a few weeks."

Trienchen watched her handsome loved one ride away. He waved his hand back toward her from a long distance.

Several times a month, Johann kept riding to the Falk home to visit Trienchen. Before winter set in, Abram knew it was time for him and his girls to pack straw along the bottom of the house, to help keep the house warm. The winters were terribly cold. One cold day before the snow blew, Trienchen also worked with her dad in hauling corn fodder bundles into the barn.

The next Thursday was hog-butchering day. Johann's girlfriend's dad had invited him to come and take part. Before daybreak the dog barked while the Falks were still eating breakfast. Trienchen looked into the darkness to see what all the racket was about. "Shut up, will you? Why are you growling?"

"Are you talking to me?" she heard from the barnyard.

"Johann, is that you? Sure sounds like it. I didn't know you were coming today. Sorry about yelling at the dog."

"Last Sunday your dad invited me over for the butchering."

"Here, let me take Jim to the barn," said Trienchen as she took the reins in her hand. "We're still at the breakfast table. You hardly had time for breakfast, did you?"

"Good morning." Father Falk smiled at him. "Have a seat at the table with our two neighbors, who are helping with the hog butchering today. We always enjoy this day together."

"Did you ever help butcher a hog?" one of the men asked.

"Nope." Johann felt uneasy about any hog subject.

Trienchen came back into the house and served him a good breakfast of hot tea, fried corn mush, and wheat bran.

After breakfast the men headed for the hog pen with a lantern and the gun. They shot the hogs before daybreak and cut them up that day. Two families, friends of the Falks named Reimer and Sawatzky, helped with all this work.

"What are you going to do with all this meat?" asked Mrs. Sawatzky. "This is more than your family will eat."

"Just don't you worry." Elizabeth laughed.

"The way it looked at the dinner table, Trienchen and the young man might be getting married later this winter. They sat real close. How about it, Trienchen?" teased Mrs. Reimer. "How old is he, anyhow, and where does he live."

"Don't you know?" responded Mrs. Sawatzky. "That's the boy a young woman found in a hog pen in Heuboden, the village in Russia. Am I right? Quite a story, if everything is true that we heard."

Immediately Elizabeth intervened: "Trienchen, go and see if the pork fat is ready to dip out of the iron kettle. It's been boiling for quite a while."

After her daughter left, Elizabeth told both women: "We do not like for anyone to mention things about Johann's birth in the presence of our daughter. Thus far we have not told her about it.

"I think she would be mighty embarrassed if she heard

people talking about it. If she had known anything of it, she would be asking me for more details.

"We've heard that Johann is self-conscious about it and doesn't like to hear of it either. In the old country he suffered so many insults and was mistreated. He had hoped that in Canada he would hear no more of being 'the hog boy.'

"Abram and I decided not to say a word of it to anyone. Johann can't help it. The poor boy never deserved all the ridicule, and as usual the gossip always goes way beyond the real truth. Here in Canada, people mentioned hardly anything of the boy's early life till he started coming to see our daughter.

"Why can't more people practice the Golden Rule? 'Do unto others as you would have them do unto you.'"

Mrs. Sawatzky felt sorry that she had brought up the subject and thoroughly apologized.

The hot fire under the black kettle made the lard boil and bubble while Trienchen stirred it with the long bowed poker. What she had heard was racking her thoughts. "The next time I am alone with Johann, I will ask him—or will I?" she muttered to herself. "Surely his forebears are among the old Mennonites."

As she came back into the kitchen, she heard the three women laughing. The neighbor women were teasing Elizabeth: "Since we are helping with the butchering, we want to be invited to your daughter's wedding. Ha-ha-ha."

"How about it, Trienchen? Are you getting married later this winter? I think you should invite us too. We like country-cured ham. Ha-ha. We hear your boyfriend has a nice farm waiting for you."

They continued in this vein and tried to make her happy as they talked well of Johann. This helped Trienchen to relax. They had fun in teasing her, but in a respectful manner.

As the day of butchering came to an end, the men cleaned up the tools and laid them aside. Trienchen went out to check on the boiling fat again. She and Johann enjoyed being together. As they watched the lard boil, she told him of the women teasing her about getting married.

"I told them I don't know anything of it. They didn't think I was telling the truth. They kept insisting, 'Surely you know,' and they laughed, giving me a hard time. What would you have told them?"

"Well, if they ask you again, tell them that maybe by next February our betrothal might be announced at church services."

Wide-eyed Trienchen looked straight into Johann's big brown eyes. They smiled at each other.

"Really, do you mean that?" she asked. "You're kidding! How do you know I approve of it? You've never asked me about marriage."

"Oh, come on, Trienchen dear. I know you love me without me asking. Nobody ever told me how or when to ask a girlfriend about marriage. I would have felt silly asking my foster dad Peters. Why didn't you ask *me* if I want to marry *you*?" Johann laughed.

"Huh? How do you think I would know what to say?" She giggled and laughed. "I've never experienced this marriage situation either."

Trienchen was bursting with joy as she entered the house and pulled her mother aside for a private word. "Mom, Johann says he wants us to be announced for our wedding at church sometime in late winter. I can hardly believe this is really happening."

"Abram!" yelled Elizabeth. "Vesper is ready before the men leave—a little snack, you know."

Johann sat at the table with the other men. Mrs. Reimer teased: "Trienchen, you sit beside your friend Johann. You might as well get used to it in case he decides to ask you to be his wife soon. How about it, Johann?"

Trienchen blushed as she accepted their humorous orders.

"Maybe next fall we can all come to help you and Trienchen butcher a hog. Do you have any hogs on your farm?"

Johann enjoyed the fun but for one definite reason he never wished to even think of having any hogs on his farm.

Also, this matter of teasing about getting married was not all fun to him. He had seen too many hardships in the different homes where he had lived. Johann had decided that marriage would be a sincere and committed step in his life.

This was a great day for these three families. Abram gave each of them a helping of puddings and bacon. "Thanks for your help," he said as they drove off. "Kind neighbors are priceless friends."

The butchering tools were stored in place until next fall's use. The crocks of lard and meat were cooled down, and the hams and bacon were ready for the smokehouse. Everyone was tired and well satisfied with the ample supply of meat.

After a hot supper of fresh sausage and spare ribs, the two lovers sat in the cold summer kitchen, talking till late. And then Johann had to go home yet and tend to his animals. He was tired but joyful as he finally knelt in a prayer of thanks to God for his beloved Trienchen. Then he crawled into bed, and deep sleep swept over him.

☙ 23 ❧

Wedding Plans

That winter Johann rode to the Falk home on Sundays whenever the weather permitted. One evening in February, Johann asked, "Why don't you go with me to my home some day, Trienchen? I can hardly wait to show you the farm. Do you think your parents would object? I'd like to see if you can cook a good meal there." Johann sat close against her to show his affectionate love.

"Well, Johann, by now you surely know that I can cook. You haven't gotten sick from any meals here, have you?"

"No, no! I've been well fed. Oh, did you ask your mother about our betrothal next Sunday?" asked Johann.

"I didn't think it was my duty to ask. What would I say? You must ask," Trienchen reminded him.

"No, you ask your mother about our plans for marriage. You see, Mom and Dad Peters are not my real parents. I wish you would ask your mother. I hope you understand."

Trienchen went to the kitchen. "Mom, Johann and I would like to be announced for marriage next Sunday, but he doesn't know how to ask the proper question. He has dreaded this for quite a while. He hoped I would know."

Elizabeth told her daughter that Johann should ask the girl's father and added, "I'll go and tell Father what you two wish to discuss."

"Come, Johann," said Trienchen. "Let's get it over with. Dad is in the big room, waiting. No one else will hear it."

During the past few months, Johann had met Abram frequently, yet somehow this was not an easy matter for him. Years ago he had decided that if he ever would become a husband, he would not betray his wife nor her parents. He would rather stay single than have a complicated married life.

"It will ruin my health if I need to see my own children being treated as I was. I hope you understand what I'm talking about, Trienchen. If we have any children, I want you to support me in all difficult situations."

"Yes, dear Johann, I understand what you are saying. I will respect and trust you and support you in making wise decisions, as the Lord guides us."

Sitting in the room with Trienchen's parents, Johann sensed a welcome attitude. Johann could feel his heart pounding as he began to speak.

"Abram, may I ask the hand of your daughter Trienchen to be my wife? I promise you that I will treat her with love and wisdom shared to me by our Lord Jesus. And we want to have our marriage announced next Sunday."

"Yes, Johann, you may have her," Abram replied. "We have no objections. God bless your life. It is fine with Elizabeth and me to have the preacher announce it at the Sunday morning services."

"Thank you, Abram," Johann said as he shook hands in parting. "Good-bye."

"Good-bye. We'll see you next Sunday, we hope."

The clock struck nine thirty as he left the house for his one-hour horseback ride home. "Good-bye, Trienchen," he said as he swung onto Jim's back

"Good-bye, Johann. Be careful! Safe home!"

Jim galloped away, carrying his rider into the dark night.

Johann never felt so thankful as he did tonight, riding in the crisp moonlit night. It was cold, but he hardly thought of it. His heart was warm as he rode mile after mile, occasionally gazing at the tiny bright stars overhead. "Could heaven be more peaceful than this?" he wondered.

He spotted his dwelling yonder, and his dog, Sport, came toward him, barking a welcome, knowing by the hoofbeats that it was his master riding Jim.

"Hi, Sport. Good dog, coming to meet Jim and me. I knew you would," he said as he patted Sport, who was stretching both front feet up on Johann.

The house was cold since the wood fire had died down during the day. Before snuggling under the covers, Johann felt a great desire to kneel beside the bed. "Blessed Lord, I thank you for this wonderful day and night. Thank you for Trienchen's true love and for your everlasting mercy and grace."

Although it was way beyond his normal time for retiring, he could not sleep as he lay there thinking of his future life.

Early in the morning Johann awoke from a beautiful dream, which he often shared later in life. He saw himself and his wife going out the driveway on a perfect Sunday morning, with the sun rising over the eastern horizon. The birds were singing, and in their little wagon they drove alongside a brook of clear blue water, with two little girls snuggly sitting on the seat beside them.

Johann could not fall asleep again. His thoughts rambled on and on. He felt so refreshed. He remembered Jacob's wonderful dream of the angels on the stairway to heaven.

While preparing his own breakfast, he told himself: "Soon I'll have someone to make meals and eat with me. I need to clean up and have everything sparkling in here and also outside, to be ready for me to bring my bride along next Monday. She wants to see her future home."

On Saturday he rode to town to buy a few necessary items for his sweetheart. He retired to bed early, preparing for the special occasion early the next morning.

"Come on, Sal! Yo-ho, Maggie!" echoed the voice of the bridegroom, calling his cows in from the meadow. It was long before daybreak when Johann sat milking, shivering by the light of the dim kerosene lantern. This was a special Sunday.

In his excitement he skipped breakfast. At the break of dawn, the wagon wheels rattled over the frozen ground of Manitoba's dirt roads. Johann Peters was on his first twelve-mile trek with his open wagon to escort his betrothed bride to church services. Always before this, he had ridden horseback.

"Good morning, good morning!" Trienchen greeted him with a smile as she came running out to meet Johann in his wagon. "You hardly had breakfast, did you?"

"No, I didn't. I'm not even hungry. I think I can live on love," he said as he looked into her bright eyes.

"No, no! You must eat, too," laughed Trienchen. "Come on in. My brother will feed your horses."

"Good morning, Johann," said Father Falk as he stretched

out his hand, welcoming him with an energetic handshake. "Sure is cold outside."

After the lovers ate breakfast together, the Falk family left for church. Trienchen climbed up into Johann's wagon, and her beau wrapped the heavy horsehide blanket around her in a lovely fashion. Both were bursting with joy as they rode together in zero weather. Johann thought that in all his twenty-six years, he never felt so blessed as to give his sweetheart her first ride with him.

The sun shone brightly as they drove the seven miles, visiting every minute about their oncoming wedding day. The big sorrel horses, Jim and Jack, were getting tired, traveling nineteen miles that morning, pulling the wagon on unpaved roads, uphill and down.

As they arrived at the churchyard, the secret was exposed. Seeing the couple, a few men said, "Oh, yes, an engagement is being announced today. Abram Falk's daughter—but who is the bridegroom? A stranger to my eyes."

"It's Mayor Peters' son, from the East Reserve area. Remember the boy they brought along from Russia years ago? He's farming all alone in the new southern settlement."

"Well, I think he will get a good farmwife to help along. Surely he must have been lonely, having no relatives nearby."

Johann greeted them with a shy "Hello" as he and Trienchen entered the meetinghouse. Inside the entrance they laid their heavy overcoats on a stack of other coats.

Now the women began to whisper in surprise about the new couple. Few betrothals occurred in this sparsely settled area in the West Reserve, west of the Red River.

When everybody was seated, the *Vorsänger* (song leader) announced the opening song: "Morgenglanz der Ewigkeit" (Morning Gleam of Eternity). The joyful voices of the congregation rang throughout the small church house.

Johann thought this song was quite fitting since it seemed like the morning of a new life for him. The bridal party sat at the front of the crowd, close by the preacher. The sermon drew emotional tears from Trienchen, as she was weeping for joy. Johann thought the sermon was a rare fulfillment in his lifetime, a new beginning.

At the end of the sermon, the preacher announced: "We have a couple here to be engaged for marriage. The bridegroom is our brother in faith Johann Peters, and the bride is our faithful sister Trienchen Falk. Does anyone here have a legal or religious reason to prevent their marriage? If you do, speak up."

There were no objections from the congregation. The preacher asked everyone to kneel in prayer, and then he called for a closing song. After the service, the happy betrothed couple climbed into their wagon and headed for the Falk home.

The custom of these folks was to leave the younger children at home during church services. Now they came running with great joy as the two drove in the lane. Seeing Trienchen's little brother and two sisters accepting Johann so graciously brought tears to his eyes.

After the noon meal with the Falk family, more church friends came to celebrate their betrothal.

"Trienchen, we are so glad to see you getting married," said neighbor Mabel Penner as they had their vesper snack of coffee and honey bread. "It's been nearly three years since there was a wedding in our area."

"Now, Johann," neighbor Jacob Wiebe said, "the step in life that you plan to take, I call it good. A better woman than Trienchen you won't find. We know her family well." He shook Johann's hand. "We must be going home to do our chores. Farewell. See you at the wedding."

Johann asked Trienchen's parents for permission for her to go home with him on Monday so he could show her the farm. He left the wagon at the Falks and rode Jim home, then came back the next morning.

Right after the noon meal, he hitched the horses to the wagon for Trienchen to ride along back to his place. She did not know what to expect, without a woman there to do the housework. But as she entered the house behind her handsome beau, she was amazed at how well kept it looked.

"Trienchen, I cannot lead you into a castle, but I hope that with the help of the Lord I may offer you a peaceful home, and that you will never wish to be anywhere else."

"Johann, my dear, I seek not a house of wealth and riches,

but of love and peace. I sense that we may be able to have a home like that. If we both work diligently, we can have a palace of love."

A cup of hot tea and a few cookies that Trienchen brought along tasted good after the long ride home.

Although it was only a few hours since they had eaten their noon meal, they remarked how splendid that this was their first meal together in their own home. "Oh, Johann, our life should go quite well when we can just always be together," said Trienchen as she cleared off the table.

"Yes, and we want to do everything we can to avoid troubled times," declared Johann, going toward the door. "I will take a quick look at the cattle, and then I must let them outside for a bit." And he went out.

Before long he brought the cattle back into the stable, where Trienchen already stood. She admired the beautiful cows. After everything was in order, they hitched up the sorrel horses again and headed for the Falk home. On the way, they stopped here and there to invite friends to their wedding. Since the folks lived far apart, this took a lot of driving time.

Here is some of the German that I have tried to translate (above). As you may see, my translation is not altogether accurate. At places in the book, I found it difficult to present the proper meanings. Thanks for your patience and understanding.

Trotzdem die unlängſt ihre Mittagsmahlzeit genoſſen hatten, mundete es vortrefflich, denn es war ihre erſte gemeinſchaftliche Mahlzeit im eigenen Heim. "Ach Johann, es wird uns aber doch ſehr ſchön gehen, wenn wir erſt für immer zuſammen ſein können," ſagte Trienchen, als ſie nach dem Eſſen aufräumte. "Ja und wir wollen alles tun, daß die trüben Zeiten fern bleiben," meinte Johann und ging zur Tür. "Ich werde noch ſchnell nach dem Vieh ſehen, denn ich muß es jetzt einfach draußen laſſen," und ging hinaus. Es dauerte nicht ſo ſehr lange, bis er mit dem Vie beim Stalle war, wo Trienchen schon stand und die schönen Kühe bewunderte. Als alles in Ordnung war, wurde der Braune wieder vorgespannt und dann ging es wieder los auf die Besuchsreise. Sie hielten hier und da an, aber da alle Freunde soweit auseinander wohnten, nahmen die Fahrten viel Zeit in Anspruch.

☙ 24 ❧

Happily Married

During the two weeks following their engagement to be married, the couple drove many more miles to the homes of friends, inviting them to their wedding at the Abram Falk home on Sunday, March 10, 1889.

The Falks were quite busy preparing every nook and corner for their first daughter's wedding. In the last three days, Trienchen baked and scrubbed and cleaned, to have everything sparkling clean and to have food ready.

At last came the final Sunday. Johann did his chores early and was on the road again, driving to the Falk homestead. "I'll bring my bride along home tonight," he thought. He was there before the late sunrise, in time to eat breakfast with them.

At mid morning, the first guests arrived, their horses frost covered from the frigid Canadian air. They drove long distances to attend the wedding.

Johann's last parents, Mayor and Susanna Peters, drove all the way from the East Reserve, and they were rather cold from the winter travel. Johann was so happy to see them again. His parents were very happy to meet the new bride.

With firm handshakes, they greeted the wedding couple: "Hello, Johann, and so this is Trienchen! So nice to meet you."

"Yes, Dad and Mother. I'm sure glad you could come in this cold weather. I'm glad it's not snowing. My, your hands feel cold, Mother."

The house was full as they squeezed together to have room for everyone. Johann and Trienchen sat comfortably on their chairs as the wedding songs echoed throughout the crowded small house. The preacher in charge explained how God had established the first marriage and planned that the man and the woman should express love and obedience to each other.

His text was the book of Ruth. "Entreat me not to leave you:

for whither you go, I will go. And where you lodge, I will lodge. Your people shall be my people, and your God my God. Where you die, I will die, and there I will be buried. The Lord do so to me and more also if anything but death part you and me" (Ruth 1:16–17).

And now the bridal party was asked to stand up in front of the preacher. Trienchen felt her face blush. Johann stood upright as the preacher presented the question: "First I ask you, Johann Peters, are you willing to take this maiden, Katharina Falk, as your wife, to love her, to care for her, and not leave her till death parts you?"

"Yes" came his answer loud and clear.

The preacher asked Trienchen the same question, and her answer was firmly "Yes." Then he pronounced them husband and wife. After he led in a prayer of blessing, the group sang another wedding hymn.

Everyone in the fellowship enjoyed the noon meal together, in accord with Mennonite custom. The cold wind blew as the guests bundled up in heavy horsehide blankets and left for home in the late afternoon.

At sundown Johann left for his home, taking along his beloved wife. As they entered the house, Johann said, "I need to start fire in the stove. I don't want you to freeze, honey!"

"No, Johann, from now on, I take care of the household duties. You take care of the cattle. Okay?"

This certainly sounded delightful to Johann, to have a willing helper. After he milked the cow, he fed the three horses and the few steers. Then he felt so lucky to enter a warm house and have someone to talk with.

When he came in, Trienchen had coffee on the stove for a warm drink. "Do you also want supper?"

"Oh, I don't know. I hate to make you work on your wedding day. But I am a trifle hungry from the long cold drive."

She spread the tablecloth, which was new for his table. "You must tell me what you want and where to find it. How do I get to the cellar and the pantry? Where do you keep your food? I can get it. You just sit down and relax."

After the late supper, they sat beside the stove, talking by candlelight till nearly midnight. The dog kept peeping at his new mistress of the house, and finally he sniffed her legs. Trienchen petted him. "It appears that the dog knows I am your friend, Johann!"

"Yeah," laughed Johann. "Sport also had a wedding feast today. He found a chunk of my good heifer meat hanging by that wall while we were away."

Sport laid his two front paws on his master's lap as Johann said, "He knows I'm talking about him. That's okay. We had a good feast today, too. Now, Sport, go and lie down in your corner and rest so you will be able to watch the cattle tomorrow again while we are away."

"Sure enough, he understands," said Trienchen. "You talk to him every day, I suppose. How nice. Now I am meddling in. He's snoring already. Ha-ha. A good dog he is."

"Well, we'd better get to bed," yawned Johann.

The next morning Johann awoke to a sound he did not understand. As he jumped up, he realized that his wife was not in bed. He was alarmed to see her firing up the woodstove. Johann was terribly embarrassed.

"How did I oversleep the first morning?" he asked as he rushed out to do his chores.

"That's perfectly okay with me," replied Trienchen. "I knew you were very tired. Should I help you with the chores?"

"No, no, it shouldn't take long. I'll let the steers outside. Sport will take care of them."

He had no fences to keep his cattle from roaming away. Sport always brought them back.

After breakfast they hitched two horses to the wagon and started for the Falk home. They wanted to help clean up after the wedding celebration and set the house back in order again.

The faces of the newlyweds were red from the cold drive as they pulled in the driveway. Trienchen's brothers and father yelled, "Here they come! Here they come! Hello. Good morning. How's it going with you?"

"Very well," answered Johann. "We wanted to help you clean up. Since we're coming so late, no doubt you're nearly done."

He surely didn't want his new father-in-law to know that he had overslept.

"Oh, that's okay, no problem," said Abram as he helped to unhitch the horses.

Trienchen's mother greeted her at the door as she entered the kitchen with a motherly kiss. One of her sisters called out: "Hi, Mrs. Peters. Come over by the stove. You're cold, I'm sure."

Only now did she realize that her name had become Trienchen Peters, not Trienchen Falk. She laughed at her sisters' fun, teasing her while she was gathering all her belongings together, to move them out of her parents' house.

It was not all that easy to load her household items on the wagon: dresses, dishes, pots and pans, a bed and a few covers, plus a few chests and a wardrobe.

After the noon meal, she exchanged farewell kisses and hugs with her mother and sisters. Sitting beside her husband on the rough farm wagon, she called out to them: "Good-bye, good-bye, Father and Mother. Thanks for all you have done for me. I don't know when we'll see each other again."

"We'll write you a letter sometime," promised her mother. "Bye-bye. Be a good wife for John, and God bless your home."

Her family gave a final wave of their hands as she looked back to her childhood home. Fond memories swept her mind and brought tears to her eyes.

In that part of Canada there was plenty of wood to keep the house warm. Trienchen still pondered one question she had from overhearing her parents' conversation one night in their bedroom. She wanted to ask Johann about it as they sat by the stove, talking, even though it was quite late.

Then she decided, "Perhaps I'd better wait till tomorrow. I know he's tired."

The next morning at the breakfast table, their lengthy visiting finally brought forth her question.

"Did you say your real mother died when you were only seven? So she was only a young mother and had no other children, I think you said."

"Well," Johann said, "I guess I should explain to you what Dad Peters once told me, about how one morning Mother Marie found me, a newborn, in a hog pen. I do not ever wish to know who my birth mother was or why she did not want me. I was hardly told all the facts. It would only create more heartaches.

"I've had enough sadness in my young years. I can forgive my birth mother for rejecting me, and I will let God be the judge of everything at the resurrection.

"As a boy, I could not understand all the mocking, being called a hog boy or rascal, but it stabbed at my heart like a knife. I do not harbor any ill feelings against those folks. But I will always remind my children or anyone else that they someday will suffer the consequences of dishing out such ridicule, possibly many years later. God will punish them someway.

"You know, Trienchen, I prefer to have this subject closed and proceed forward, having a happy married life."

"Yes, Johann, I understand." Trienchen wept tears of sympathy for the mistreated boy who grew up to be her husband.

She fully decided that she must do her best to make a good married life with Johann. "He surely deserves it," she told herself.

God's ways are far beyond human understanding. We do not know why this forsaken child's life was spared, and why he suffered so much. Nevertheless, God was watching over Johann through all his years and brought him into a satisfying marriage with Trienchen, who accepted him without reservations. And they truly loved and treasured all their children and grandchildren.*

ᴄᴙ The End ᴙᴐ

---

* After marriage in March 1889, Johann Peters and Katharina Falk had ten children, one of whom died in infancy. Katharina died in 1915 at age 47. In 1916 the widow Nettie Wall brought two children into the family when Johann married her, and they had seven more children, one of whom died in infancy. In 1946 Johann died at age 83 in Lowe Farm, Manitoba. Nettie died in 1971 at age 80. Margaret Maier, *John Peters Family Tree, 1863–1993* (n.p.: the author, 1993), lists Johann's descendants.